MATERNAL EMOTIONS

A PSYCHOSOMATIC MEDICINE MONOGRAPH

MATERNAL EMOTIONS

A Study of Women's Feelings Toward Menstruation, Pregnancy, Childbirth, Breast Feeding, Infant Care, and Other Aspects of Their Femininity

by **NILES NEWTON**, Ph.D.

RESEARCH ASSOCIATE IN OBSTETRICS
SCHOOL OF MEDICINE, UNIVERSITY OF PENNSYLVANIA

PAUL B. HOEBER, Inc.

MEDICAL BOOK DEPARTMENT OF HARPER & BROTHERS

Published with the sponsorship of the American Psychosomatic
Society, Inc., and the approval of the Editorial Board
of PSYCHOSOMATIC MEDICINE

```
Paperback editions:

First Printing — 1963
Second Printing — 1966
Third Printing — 1969
Fourth Printing — 1971
Fifth Printing — 1972
Sixth Printing — 1973
Seventh Printing — 1975
Eight Printing — 1975
Ninth Printing — 1976
```

Library of Congress catalog card number: 55-5373

THIS BOOK IS DEDICATED

To My Parents—who educated and encouraged me

To My Husband—who helped me constantly

To My Children—who taught me the deep satisfaction of being a mother

CONTENTS

Preface   ix

Acknowledgments   xi

1. The Problem   1

2. Research Methods   5

3. Women's Feelings About Menstruation   14

4. Women's Feelings About Pregnancy   24

5. Women's Feelings About Childbirth   30

6. Women's Feelings About Breast Feeding   43

7. Women's Feelings About Care of Their Babies   59

8. Women's Envy of Men   73

9. Sexual Intercourse: Its Relation to the Rest of Women's
    Sexual Role   85

10. Biological Femininity versus Cultural Femininity   95

11. Conclusions   102

    Appendix A—Ways of Encouraging the Expression of
                Personal Feelings   105
             B—The Interpretation and Measurement of
                Personal Feelings   113
             C—The Statistical Methods   123
             D—Statistical Details of the Findings of This
                Research   125

    Index   129

PREFACE

Woman's sexual emotions are concerned with more aspects of her life than her relations with the opposite sex. Although these broader aspects of sexual behavior and feeling affect many parts of woman's life, they are generally depreciated; and, when not completely ignored, are regarded as separate and unrelated parts of her biological function. Implicit in this attitude is the lingering cultural discrimination against woman. In many ways she is regarded as a carbon copy of man. Often, her distinctive sexual characteristics are emphasized only insofar as they are of interest to the opposite sex.

There are several assumptions behind this cultural attitude that deserve exploration. Some of these are investigated in this study. The first is the truth of the "atomistic" theory of women's sexuality—the degree of correlation that exists between attitudes toward different aspects of womanhood. Are women's feelings toward sexual intercourse, menstruation, pregnancy, childbirth, breast feeding, and infant care related to each other? Does acceptance by a woman of one important part of her life tend to be accompanied by acceptance of other parts?

The next aspect of the problem is the relation of women's sexuality to our cultural depreciation of the female role. Is envy of men related to other undesirable sexual attitudes in women?

Another aspect explored is the relation of women's attitudes toward sexual function to the performance of them. For instance, does the woman who has positive attitudes toward her wider sexual role actually have fewer obstetrical and gynecological problems?

Two methods are used to explore these questions. The first is the search for previously established facts that might have bearing on the problem. Pertinent information was found in published medical, psychological, and sociological research as well as in several other fields. Studies using controlled and experimental methods of inquiry are reviewed and their findings form an integral part of the chain of evidence presented in this book.

The second method used is a research project specifically planned to give information about the basic questions involved. Essentially this research consisted of studying a group of healthy, normal, childbearing women through psychological interview and medical records, and analyzing the data objectively.

By training I am a psychologist; my research has been primarily medical. This book represents an effort to combine these two fields and several others in the study of women's wider sexual role. I first became aware of the importance of using several branches of knowledge during my study of one aspect of women's role—breast feeding. An interest in this problem led me not only into pediatrics and obstetrics, but also into psychology, psychoanalysis, anthropology, sociology, and physiology; and to my surprise I found much pertinent and basic research in the library of a school of veterinary medicine. This was a valuable lesson.

It has been my hope that this book may show, as many others have done before, the value of breaking down the barriers of habit and ignorance which separate one field of knowledge from another. It was also my hope to demonstrate once again that intimate human emotions can be *fruitfully* studied by controlled, statistical or experimental methods.

My deepest hope, however, is that this book may be of some value to those interested in helping women to have better health and more satisfying lives—to those concerned with problems of obstetrics, gynecology, pediatrics, psychology, psychiatry, sociology, education, and legislation. The book will serve its purpose if, by its organized presentation of pertinent facts, it suggests some new approaches to old problems.

NILES NEWTON

ACKNOWLEDGMENTS

I am deeply indebted to the Department of Obstetrics and Gynecology of Jefferson Medical College and particularly to Thaddeus L. Montgomery, M.D., who permitted me to do research in his maternity wards before I had other medical school affiliations. I would also like to thank the whole staff of the maternity wards of Jefferson Hospital for the privilege of working in their midst.

I would particularly like to thank Percival M. Symonds, Ph.D., Arthur T. Jersild, Ph.D., Ernest G. Osborne, Ph.D., Stanley M. Bysshe, M.D., Margaret Mead, Ph.D., Lewis C. Scheffey, M.D., Thaddeus L. Montgomery, M.D., Franklin L. Payne, M.D., Douglas P. Murphy, M.D., Harry Fields, M.D., and the publisher for going over this manuscript when it was in its formative stages of development. Their suggestions, encouragements, and criticisms were most helpful. The statistical advice of Helen Walker, Ph.D., was appreciated, and so was the help of Daniel Clarke in doing the statistical computations. I am also appreciative of the grant of a Public Health Service Research Fellowship of the National Institute of Mental Health which made the initial parts of this study possible. I also wish to thank the C. V. Mosby Co. for permission to quote their publications and *Fortune* for permission to quote The Fortune Survey of August and September, 1946.

Preparation of this manuscript would have been almost impossible without the assistance of Michael Newton, M.D., my husband, and Helen Coady, the typist, who have helped this work grow from a research outline into a Ph.D. dissertation, and then into a book.

MATERNAL EMOTIONS

CHAPTER 1

THE PROBLEM

Our society has a tendency to ignore or belittle women's emotions toward their unique biological functions. All sorts of devices have been invented to try to hide menstruation, and active measures are taken to reduce the number of pregnancies. Potent drugs are often administered to render women unconscious at birth and to suppress the secretion of milk. After delivery the baby is usually removed from its mother, since it is considered too much of a burden for her, and is only returned to her care after several days have elapsed.

The second large area of feeling that we tend to ignore is the feelings engendered in women by cultural depreciation of their abilities and contributions. Job discrimination on the basis of sex is deeply ingrained in our society. For instance, United States Census reports show that women who have had one or more years of college generally earn less than men who have failed to complete grade school. At the same time the importance of woman's traditional role is minimized. For instance novels, magazines, television, and movies usually deal with women in relation to their attractiveness to men, but seldom portray the worthwhileness of their struggles as homemakers and mothers.

When these large areas of women's feelings are not completely ignored, they tend to be viewed in a narrow, subdivided way. Thus a mother's alarm at caring for her newborn baby is often viewed as something quite apart from her disgust at menstruation, her agony at childbirth, and her wish to be a man.

1

THE PROBLEMS TO BE STUDIED

Women's feelings toward all aspects of their female physical role are studied together in this study. The basic questions are:

"Are women's feelings toward menstruation, pregnancy, childbirth, breast feeding, infant care, and the desirability of being a woman related to other physical, psychological, or social phenomena?"

"What does this mean in terms of helping women to better health and more satisfying lives?"

These general questions can be broken up into numerous specific questions of the following types:

"Is the woman who dislikes menstruation also the one who is most likely to have menstrual pain?"

"Are obstetrical complications more likely to be found in a mother who resents her woman's lot in life than in one who enjoys being a woman?"

"Is the mother's wish to be a man related to her desire for a boy baby or her dislike of baby care?"

"Does the woman who wants to breast feed her baby actually tend to have different emotions toward babies or a different obstetrical history?"

"Is the woman who complains about menstruation, pregnancy, childbirth, breast feeding, and infant care also the woman who tends to marry late or who works after marriage?"

CURRENT POINTS OF VIEW

Although there has been relatively little objective, well-controlled research in this field of inquiry, psychoanalysts, psychologically minded doctors, and anthropologists have suggested a wealth of insights and possibilities. Particularly prolific have been women of the psychoanalytic school of thought who have emphasized the fundamental importance of such events as first menstruation and menopause, pregnancy, childbirth, and breast feeding.

Sylvia Payne states that real understanding of women's psychological problem can come *only* through recognizing the importance of their reproductive functions. She says: ". . . We shall not understand the psychological problems of woman until we understand more of the factors which interfere with the pattern and rhythm of her functions of reproduction. Her psyche is more closely attuned to her body than man's, whether in dealing with her sexual functions or expressing itself in sublimation."

Karen Horney makes this point forcefully when she protests against the tendency to view women's emotional experiences as similar but inferior to those of a male. She writes: ". . . And what about motherhood? And the blissful consciousness of bearing a new life within oneself? And the ineffable happiness of the increasing expectation of the appearance of this new being? And the joy when it finally makes its appearance and one holds it for the first time in one's arms? And the deeply pleasurable feeling of satisfaction in suckling it and the happiness of the whole period when the infant needs her care?"

Helene Deutsch sees woman's role in less joyful terms, believing that the essence of feminine psychology is masochism, narcissism, and passivity. Yet she, too, emphasizes the emotional impact of such events as menarche and menopause, intercourse and childbearing.

Sigmund Freud himself also believed that much of woman's psychological development was due to her emotional reactions to her own female body. He, like Deutsch, assumed that woman's reaction was essentially a negative one. However, instead of emphasizing self love and the welcoming of pain, he emphasized more the deep feelings of inadequacy and envy that he believed women felt in their lack of a penis. Thus he writes: "Her whole development may be said to take place under the influence of her envy for the penis. She begins by making vain attempts to do the same as boys, and later, with greater success, makes efforts to compensate herself for the defect—efforts which may lead in the end to a normal feminine attitude."

Margaret Mead, with the perspective of an anthropologist, suggests that although middle-class neurotic women of contemporary occidental society frequently feel wounded by lack of male sexual equipment, this need not be true of all women. She points out that such feelings of envy develop against a general background of overrewards for the male position and a prudish use of clothing.

Women's feelings of inadequacy compared to men would naturally develop more easily in a society where woman's reproductive role is disparaged. In our society, Dr. Mead notes, the rhythms of the female are considered primarily a nuisance and a handicap—to be muted, transcended, or ignored. In some other societies festive ceremonies may often mark first menstruation and childbirth. Pregnancy is not disguised and breast feeding may be an open and casual act.

Grantly Dick Read has seized upon the possibility of positive values in women's reproductive experiences. He has written forcefully about the deep joy and satisfaction the whole childbearing experience can bring to women—provided they are adequately prepared and are given considerate help. His natural childbirth movement has spread to many parts of the world—in countries as far apart as England and South Africa, Sweden, and the United States. The popularity of his ideas indicates that some occidental women may be eager to view their reproductive processes as important, forthright, and meaningful parts of their lives.

SUMMARY

Our society has a tendency to ignore or belittle menstruation, pregnancy, childbirth, breast feeding, motherliness, and women's work. What effect do these negative attitudes have on women themselves?

Psychoanalysts, psychologically minded doctors, and anthropologists have suggested a wealth of insights and possibilities in regard to certain aspects of this problem.

REFERENCES

1. DEUTSCH, HELENE   *The Psychology of Women.*   New York, Grune & Stratton, 1944, Vol. I; 1945, Vol. II.
2. FREUD, S.   *An Outline of Psychoanalysis.*   New York, Norton, Inc. 1949, p. 97.
3. HORNEY, KAREN   The flight from womanhood. *Internat. J. Psycho-Analysis 7:*324, 1926.
4. MEAD, MARGARET   *From the South Seas.*   New York, Morrow, 1939.
5. MEAD, MARGARET   *Male and Female.*   New York, Morrow, 1949.
6. PAYNE, SYLVIA M.   A conception of femininity. *Brit. J. M. Psychol. 15:*18, 1935.
7. READ, G. D.   *Childbirth Without Fear.*   New York, Harper & Brothers, 1944.
8. READ, G. D.   *The Birth of a Child.*   New York, Vanguard, 1950.

CHAPTER 2

RESEARCH METHODS

The choice of research methods always rests on basic assumptions. There were three basic assumptions that led to the research methods used in this study:

1. Human feelings can be fruitfully studied by controlled, statistical methods.

2. Generalizations from extremes to normal should be avoided whenever possible.

3. Mind and body are an interacting unit and should be studied together whenever possible.

THE CASE FOR CONTROLLED, STATISTICAL METHODS

At present the psychology of emotions is still partly in the philosophical stage of development. The most popular methods used for obtaining information are essentially the same as those of Aristotle. Groups of phenomena are observed in an uncontrolled manner, and then a system of knowledge is built on the basis of intuition and reasoning. There has been a lack of interest in putting these theories to rigorous and repeated test against a wide range of facts collected in an unbiased manner.[1, 7]

Although very great insights are often developed by these methods, misconceptions are also perpetuated. For instance, Aristotle said that the heart acts as a furnace heating and churning the blood, a theory clearly based on some anatomical observations. Galen followed Aristotle's lead, and their views were used to justify the practice of bleeding sick people—a practice that continued for centuries and at one time was the

5

physician's chief method of treating disease. Even when Harvey discovered the circulation of the blood by painstaking, extensive observation and experimentation he was denounced because his views did not agree with those of Aristotle and Galen.[2]

Yet there continues to be a widespread belief that such philosophical methods are unavoidable in the study of feelings and emotions. These are deemed too variable, individual, and private for controlled scientific study.

However, three hundred years ago this situation must have been equally true for the physical scientist. For instance, chemical reactions as they occur in nature are extremely complex and hard to observe accurately. The chemist does have the advantage of working with material that can be manipulated experimentally to a greater extent, but the emotional scientist has the advantage of having the material of his interest in the process of formation all around him. He does not have to find it or mine it long after the events that led to its natural formation have occurred. Thus the emotional scientist, like the astronomer, gains more from observing "natural" experiments, and does not have to lean so heavily on artificial experiments.

Nor is the infinite variability of the emotions a reason against applying scientific methods. Human physiology is also so individual that a bloodhound can trace a person by the smell given off by his unique physiological reactions. In spite of this individual variability which appears in almost all physiological reactions, physiology is thoroughly scientific in its orientation.

The methods and tools of the physical scientist have been built up by the combined inventiveness of more than ten generations of scientists of many nations. The greatest challenge that lies before the emotional scientist is the invention of more adequate tools and methods. Emotional scientists who are living today cannot expect to get anything but very crude understanding, comparable to the crude concepts arrived at by the early physical scientists. Many of their answers will be outmoded with the invention of better methods, *but* those better methods will have been developed because of their efforts. In this lies their more permanent contribution to their field of interest.

THE POSSIBLE DANGER OF GENERALIZING FROM EXTREME TO AVERAGE

The second assumption upon which this research is based is that there may be danger in generalizing from extreme cases to more average cases. Certainly, valuable knowledge has been gained by studying people who seek help from psychologists, psychiatrists, and psychoanalysts, or who volunteer for psychological research in the hope of getting help with their worries. Emotional reactions of all human beings have certain similarities; however, there is no proof that emotional phenomena in disturbed persons are *only* quantitatively different from those who seek no aid in handling their emotions.

The difference in their emotions may be one of *kind* as well as *degree*. Indeed, many observations lead us to believe that in any continuum qualitative changes occur along with quantitative ones. Thus as the size of the wave length decreases, its nature changes so radically that we call one end of the continuum wireless waves, the middle portion visible light, and the other end x-rays. Or in the psychological field the *type* as well as the *number* of problems a child solves varies with his I.Q.[5] The child with a high I.Q. has something different as well as something more than the child with low I.Q. Similarly, a woman who seeks psychiatric help may have a somewhat different *kind* of emotion about motherhood as well as a different *degree* of emotion. Refusal to recognize the distortion due to the study of specialized groups may lead to extreme or inaccurate conclusions.

THE ADVANTAGE OF STUDYING MIND AND BODY TOGETHER

The third assumption upon which this research is based is that mind and body are an interacting unit and should be studied together whenever possible. There is abundant evidence that physical factors as well as psychological factors influence the individual's reaction to situations that he confronts. True, the extensive, well-controlled experiments of Rhine and his associates indicate that there seem to be some extraphysical components in human beings.[3] However, most of the evidence we have indicates that mind and body usually act as a unit. It seems probable, therefore, that the greatest understanding can be achieved when both physical and mental factors are considered together.

THE METHODS OF RESEARCH USED IN THIS STUDY

It is because of these three basic beliefs that this investigator chose to collect objective mental and physical data on nonvolunteer women who were not known to have sought psychological help.

The following account of the research methods is a brief summary. Additional information will be found in Appendixes A, B, and C. The complete details of the research methods are available elsewhere.[6]

THE WOMEN STUDIED

Two hundred and forty-six mothers of newborn babies were interviewed in the rooming-in wards of the Jefferson Hospital in Philadelphia. The interview with the first 56 mothers was confined to exploring fruitful ways of getting information from the mothers and developing techniques. Then 190 mothers were interviewed with the same interview form, using questions of standardized wording. There was a slight difference in the nature of verbal reply given by women interviewed second in the room or during the later part of the puerperium; therefore, the final statistical analysis was done on the 123 mothers who were interviewed first in the room and on the first and second postpartum days.

The interviews took place between April, 1950, and March, 1951. Practical reasons, such as the free time that the investigator had available, dictated which mother should be interviewed. However, no mothers were used unless they and their babies were well enough so that the baby was actually in the room with the mother.

Rooming-in was compulsory for all healthy ward mothers and babies, and there was an emphasis on psychological instead of pharmacological methods of pain control in labor. This natural childbirth and rooming-in program may have attracted an atypical type of woman to the private maternity service, but did not seem to influence the group of ward mothers studied in this research. Registration interviews with every mother registering for ward maternity accommodation indicated that the hospital was chosen for such mundane reasons as nearness and its easy payment plan.

The final research group consisted of 123 mothers, the majority of whom were married Protestant Negro multiparas. However, the group included 28 unmarried or separated mothers, 35 mothers of first babies, 20 white women, and 23 Catholic women. About half the group were born in the South and half in the North. The research group represented the four occupational categories quite well. Twenty-two were classified as dependents, 37 as unskilled, 26 as semiskilled, and 23 as skilled, white collar, or professional, with 15 of unknown occupational level. No significant differences were found between Negro and white mothers in their expressed feelings toward their biologically determined role;

whereas significant differences were found between different age groups and socioeconomic groups.*

THE DATA OBTAINED BY INTERVIEW

Considerable effort was made to approach the mothers in such a way that they would feel free to express their feelings (see Appendix A for a detailed discussion). Seventy-seven per cent of the mothers were fully cooperative, in the opinion of the interviewer, and in only 2 per cent was rapport considered poor throughout. No interview was stopped or discarded because of lack of good rapport, as it was felt that this might introduce a subjective method of discarding data.

The mothers were asked about their feelings toward the following aspects of their lives:

Menstruation
Pregnancy
Childbirth
Breast feeding
Rooming-in care of the baby
Satisfaction in women's role in life
Wish to be a man

Feelings toward sexual intercourse were also assessed in a few mothers for the purpose of an exploratory study. Information about job history, attendance at mothers' classes, satisfaction in the sex of the child, and number of children considered "ideal" was also obtained.

All the replies the mothers made to the questions were written down verbatim as nearly as possible.

The women's answers to each question were then individually sorted into clearly defined categories by a judge who did not know the women, their case records, or what they had answered to the other questions (see Appendix B for a detailed discussion).

OTHER SOURCES OF DATA

The following information was obtained from the medical case record:

Physical Data

Age of onset of menstruation
Duration of menstruation

* Because of deep-seated prejudice there may be a tendency to feel that a group composed of Negro and white people is more heterogeneous than a group composed of different age groups or socioeconomic groups. Kinsey's work, as well as this study, indicate that quite the opposite may be true. Kinsey writes: "It is already clear that Negro and white patterns for comparable social levels are close if not identical."

Pain during menstruation
Degree of menstrual flow
Previous miscarriages and abortions
Complications of this pregnancy
Duration of labor
Complications of childbirth
Anesthesia or analgesia administered during childbirth
Weight gain of baby in mother's care
Adequacy of breast feeding during hospital stay
Adequacy of breast feeding six weeks after delivery

Sociological and Psychological Data

Number of children
Nervous symptoms after six weeks of living with baby
Marital status
Age of marriage
Age of mother
Region of birth
Race
Religion
Occupation of husband or of the mother herself

In addition, the Terman Masculinity-Femininity Test was given to some women for the purpose of doing an exploratory study.

The material obtained from medical case records usually fell into two obvious divisions. For instance, complications of childbirth were either present or absent. On continuous data like age, the cases were divided into categories in such a way that a fairly extreme group of reasonable statistical size was separated from the rest of the cases. Thus all the information was put into dichotomous categories.

STATISTICS

This mass of information gathered from interview, medical case record, and from the Masculinity-Femininity Test was put on IBM cards. These cards were electrically sorted in such a way that the relationship between various factors could be studied. Phi correlation coefficients were used as a measure of the degree of relationship, and Chi squares were calculated to determine the level of significance or probability.

Research studies that go into unexplored fields as this one does may lose much valuable suggestive data by ignoring relationships that have moderate probabilities. At the same time, of course, relationships that are very unlikely to have occurred by chance should be weighed much more heavily. For this reason five different levels of significance were calculated. These represent the different levels of confidence that can be placed on the findings (see Appendix C for a detailed discussion of statistical methods).

LIMITATIONS OF THIS STUDY

Medical clinicians until recently put great emphasis on the *number* of cases. A scientific report covering 1000 cases was considered *ipso facto* more valuable than a report covering 100 cases. Now it is realized that 100 cases that truly represent the problem studied can be much more important from the scientific point of view than 1000 cases chosen in a biased fashion.

This fundamental change in scientific thought is well put by Colin White in a recent paper in the *British Medical Journal*. He writes: ". . . Faith in the reliability of large samples was so general among medical workers as to seem almost an unofficial extension of the Hippocratic Oath." Now it is realized that: "Quality in general is more important than quantity; if the sampling is biased, an increase in the number of individuals may merely commit you more and more firmly to a false hypothesis."

For instance, in this study the final 123 cases were probably quite sufficient to show the major tendencies to be found in the type of woman that frequents the *wards* of Jefferson Hospital. Studying 500 of them would have added only little new to our knowledge. However, a study of 100 women who frequent the private rooms of Jefferson Hospital would have added considerably to our knowledge for from them we would have learned to what extent the findings could be generalized to a different type of woman.

The limitation of this research lies not so much in the number of cases, but in the fact that only one limited segment of the total United States population was studied. Studies on other types of women might quite possibly find the same tendencies as those found in this research; but until such research is done, no definite conclusion can be made.

In this connection it should be noted that this research is not a study of *incidence* but a study of *relationship*. At no time will attempts be made to say that *x* percentage of women had positive feelings and *y* percentage of women had negative feelings. Instead, interest centers on the relation of one emotion to another emotion in the same women. For instance, the *number* of women who found childbirth horrible and disliked the care of their babies might be quite different in a group of rich women from the number in the group used in this research. Nevertheless, in *both* groups the women who found childbirth horrible might also tend to be the ones who disliked the care of their babies.

OTHER SOURCES OF EVIDENCE

In addition to this research, psychological, medical, and sociological literature was studied in order to collect various experimental and statistical facts that might have a bearing on the problem of women's feelings toward their biologically determined role. Much of the most important evidence discussed in this book comes from these sources.

SUMMARY

Bias, illusion, and error can only be discovered through the application of rigorous scientific methods. Therefore the data for this study were collected in a controlled manner and subjected to statistical tests for significance.

Generalizations from extreme to average can be misleading. Therefore only nonvolunteer women who were not known to have sought psychological help were used in this study.

Mind and body usually act together as a unit. Therefore, the physical and the psychological were studied together.

Healthy mothers of newborn babies were interviewed in the maternity wards of Jefferson Hospital in Philadelphia. Records were made of what they said about menstruation, pregnancy, childbirth, breast feeding, rooming-in care of the baby, envy of men, and other aspects of their female role. Other data were obtained from medical case records. These facts were categorized in an objective manner, recorded on IBM cards, and statistically analyzed.

Psychological, medical, and sociological literature was studied to collect experimental and statistical facts that might have a bearing on the problem at hand.

REFERENCES

1. ELLIS, A. An introduction to the principles of scientific psychoanalysis. *Genet. Psychol. Monogr. 41*:147, 1950.
2. HAGGARD, H. W. *The Doctor in History*. New Haven, Yale, 1934.
3. *Journal of Parapsychology*, Volumes 1 to 16; 1937 to 1952.
4. KINSEY, A. C., *et al. Sexual Behavior in the Human Male*. Philadelphia, Saunders, 1948, p. 393.

5. MERRILL, M. A. On the relation of intelligence to achievement in the case of mentally retarded children. *Compar. Psychol. Monogr.* No. 10, Vol. 2, 1924.

6. NEWTON, NILES *Attitudes of Mothers of Newborn Babies Toward Their Biological Feminine Functions.* Ph.D. Dissertation, Columbia University, 1952. Available from University Microfilms, 313 North First Street, Ann Arbor, Michigan.

7. OBERNDORF, C. P. Unsatisfactory results of psychoanalytic therapy. *Psychoanalyt. Quart.* 19:393, 1950.

8. WHITE, C.   Sampling in medical research. *Brit. M. J.* 2:1284, 1953.

CHAPTER 3

WOMEN'S FEELINGS
ABOUT MENSTRUATION

FINDINGS OF OTHER RESEARCH STUDIES

A large body of objective evidence indicates that women's feelings*
are closely related to the physical course of the menstrual cycle and conversely that the physical course of the menstrual cycle is related to
women's feelings.

EFFECT OF MENSTRUATION ON EMOTIONS AND BEHAVIOR

McCance, Luff, and Widdowson collected day-to-day records of 167
normal women covering 780 complete menstrual cycles. They found that
subjective feelings of fatigue varied tremendously with the menstrual
cycle, as did headaches, backaches, and abdominal pain. Depression was
often recorded just before or during the early part of menstruation, but
this tendency was not so overwhelming as had been previously reported
on the basis of the less accurate questionnaire method. There were also
minor variations in feelings of elation, which corresponded somewhat to
the rise and fall of sexual feelings. The tendency to cry was found to
be uncommon but cyclical. Irritability was less common than fatigue but
it, too, showed rhythmic variations with a sudden drop between the first
and fifth day of the period. Sexual feeling was cyclical in both married

* The terms "emotion" and "feeling" will be used more or less interchangeably
throughout this book. Actually, the term "emotion" connotes strong feelings; and
the term "feeling" conveys the meaning of a less excited emotional state.

14

and unmarried women. The frequency of sexual intercourse in married women also varied with the menstrual cycle.

A close relationship between hormonal changes and psychic content has been suggested by Benedek and Rubenstein. Using psychoanalysis and the vaginal smear methods of hormone assay, they studied 152 menstrual cycles occurring in 15 women patients. They concluded that estrogen and progesterone levels seemed to be related to material brought out by psychoanalysis.

MENSTRUATION AND ABILITY TO WORK

The relation of the menstrual cycle to actual ability to work appears to be complex. The McCance, Luff, and Widdowson research indicates that there are marked variations in the effort required to do intellectual work. The women in their study reported that it was most difficult to work on the first day of menstruation. Johnson found that girls learning to walk a tightwire did poorly during menstruation, followed by a rapid rise in achievement thereafter. Sowton and Meyers found that menstruation made little difference on short objective tests. Smith found that differences in quality and quantity of production in aircraft and garment industries did not appear to be related to menstrual function, although absence rate did vary with menstruation in some groups. Billings, who did pedimetric studies on women who had no work obligations, found a consistent postmenstrual burst of activity which gradually declined to the time of the succeeding menstrual period. It is possible that women are able to perform equally well during all phases of the menstrual cycle but are less desirous of doing so during some portions of it unless strongly motivated.

EFFECT OF EMOTIONS ON MENSTRUATION

Not only does the physical menstrual cycle bring with it emotional manifestations, but also there is considerable evidence that mental factors influence the nature of menstruation. A study of 150 mental patients showed that depressive moods were associated with lack of menstrual flow, while expansive moods, agitation, and worry were apt to be associated with profuse flow.[1] Of 60 Army nurses on Bataan and Corregidor in World War II, 50 per cent had menstrual disorders.[22] Amenorrhea occurred in 14.8 per cent of 1042 white women in Santo Tomas Internment Camp in Manila, Philippines.[22] The menses of these women had stopped since the outbreak of the war. Food shortages, which might have accounted for the amenorrhea on physical grounds, did not develop until later.

Fear without changes in environment can also influence menstruation. Delayed menstruation in women who fear pregnancy is a well-known and well-recognized phenomenon.[6, 14] Menninger gives a case history of a woman who repeatedly started to menstruate when undesired sexual intercourse seemed imminent.

Emotional shocks may have a profound influence on menstruation. Novak and Harnik,[17] in treating 45 cases of psychogenic bleeding, elicited a history of psychic trauma leading to the bleeding in all but one. Loeser reports on 4 women who always menstruated regularly but who missed a period after an emotional shock. Histological examination of a biopsy showed that the endometrium was in that state of development it would have normally reached at the time of the shock.

Motherly emotions may be related to the quantity and duration of menstrual flow. Further details about these findings can be found in Chapter 7, where enjoyment of the care of the baby is discussed.

THE NEUROTIC PERSONALITY AND MENSTRUATION

There is a good deal of research on the occurrence of menstrual pain and its relation to personality factors. The most outstanding of these studies is by Wittkower and Wilson because it is one of the few studies to investigate childhood experiences that makes use of the control or check group. Fifty-seven unselected patients with painful menstruation (primary dysmenorrhea) and 30 controls (primigravidas) who never had experienced severe menstrual pain were each interviewed for about two hours. The interview centered around the biographical history and a complete verbatim report was kept. As children the menstrual pain group showed four times as much psychological maladjustment as the control group. As adults the menstrual pain group showed a high excess of two main personality types— ". . . the first characterized by a deep resentment of their feminine role; the second obviously immature physically and either shy and shut in or chronically anxious and complaining." Of the married women with menstrual pain only 6 out of 26 were well adjusted sexually, whereas 22 out of 30 of the control group were well adjusted sexually.

Other research studies indicate that personality factors are closely associated with menstrual pain. Cunningham studied more than 14,000 University of California college girls. She found that girls having menstrual pain not only had less healthy physical records but also were more apt to suffer from headaches, insomnia, and functional nervous disorders. These disorders were all more frequent in those having severe pain than in those having mild pain. Rose gave Bell Adjustment Inventories to 266 college women and found significant differences in emotional adjustment. Girls with no pain had the best adjustment scores, those with a little pain had average scores, and those with severe pain had the poorest adjustment scores. Haman did a study on pain thresholds of 400 people. He found that women who had menstrual pain were quicker to complain of "pain" than other groups.

EFFECT OF HYPNOSIS AND PSYCHOTHERAPY ON MENSTRUATION

The last evidence we have of the extraordinarily clear relationship between menstruation and emotion comes from psychotherapy and hypnosis. Menstruation has been altered by relatively simple psychological operations.

Time of bleeding can be altered by hypnosis. Heyer made a practice of regulating menstruation of artists so that the period would not occur at the time of an important performance. The period was either skipped or postponed when he put such suggestions in the patient's mind in the third degree of hypnosis. There are also case reports of the length of the menstrual cycle being regulated to start on a certain day of the month, regardless of the number of days in the month.

Dunbar reports that it is well known and well accepted knowledge among hypnotists that many cases of amenorrhea or profuse bleeding can be cured in one session. Cures by hypnosis can be dramatic. One patient who had suffered from amenorrhea for two and a half years was induced to menstruate the first day of each month beginning at 7:00 A.M. and lasting for three days. Another case had had profuse bleeding lasting two weeks and recurring at intervals of only one week for a period of six months. One hypnosis session stopped the bleeding and a second session regulated the menstrual cycle. It stayed regulated for years.[5]

Cures by hypnosis have not been uniformly successful, however. Heyer points out that a colorless command to menstruate will not bring about the desired results—the whole experience of menstruation must be vividly described to the patient. In a case reviewed by Dunbar, an attempt to induce abortion by hypnosis failed although previously the woman's menstrual cycle had been influenced by hypnotic suggestion. Instead of aborting the woman wet her bed.

As early as 1925 there were reports of rapid cures of painful menstruation through hypnosis.[5] More recently Kroger and Freed have reported that they relieved 7 out of 9 women of menstrual pain by hypnosis with or without hypnoanalysis and age regression, when these cases had been intractable to the usual physical ministrations.

Even superficial psychotherapy is reported to be helpful in relieving menstrual pain. Novak and Harnik[18] treated 247 cases with psychological exploration. One hundred and thirty-two cases were reported as cured and 67 were relieved. Hunter and Rolf found that they relieved as many cases of menstrual pain with placebos, suggestion, and hypnosis as by localized medical and surgical means. The main factor seemed to be the confidence of the patient.

RESULTS OF THIS STUDY

Previous research gives clear evidence that emotions influence menstruation and that the menstrual cycle influences emotions. This research study concentrates on emotions toward menstruation itself.

Women were considered to have negative feelings about menstruation if they said unpleasant things about menstruation. Such women complained about weakness, backaches, pain, upset stomach. Some used extreme adjectives like "terrible" and "suffering."

Women were considered to have positive feelings about menstruation if they did not complain about it. They spoke of their feelings in such terms as "normal," "natural," "all right," "no trouble at all"—or even "good" and "fine."

Women with negative feelings toward menstruation were found to differ from women with positive feelings toward menstruation in twelve different ways.

These differences are summarized in the following paragraphs. Statistical calculations show that all of these differences are quite unlikely to have occurred by chance ($p < 0.2$). The ones that are very unlikely to have occurred by chance ($p < 0.05$) have an asterisk beside them. The statistical details can be found in Appendix D.

Feelings toward men and masculinity were related to feelings toward menstruation. Women who spoke of menstruation in favorable terms more often wished for girl babies while those who complained about menstruation were more likely to want boys.* The wish to be a man occurred slightly more frequently in women who disliked menstruation. Women who were positive about menstruation very seldom said they wished they were men.

Motherly feelings were also related to feelings about menstruation. Women who were positive about menstruation usually liked looking after their babies in the hospital, while women who complained about menstruation were more likely to show a dislike for rooming-in.* Women who complained about menstruation were more likely to think that more children in the family would be "ideal,"* but in reality they had actually produced fewer children than those women who accepted menstruation as natural.* The negative group also tended to be younger,* perhaps because older women who dislike being motherly are not apt to be found in a maternity ward.

As might be expected, women with negative feelings toward menstruation reported *menstrual pain* much more frequently than those who had positive feelings toward menstruation.* Those who disliked menstruation also were more likely to feel that their menstrual periods lasted longer. However, it was women with positive feelings toward menstruation who reported more nervous symptoms six weeks postpartum*—a relationship which is hard to understand.

The physical course of childbearing was also related to the feelings about menstruation. The women who complained about menstruation were more apt to have miscarriages.* They had fewer completely normal births.* Analgesia or anesthesia was more likely to be used during their labors.

PRACTICAL APPLICATION

PSYCHOLOGICAL KNOWLEDGE IN GYNECOLOGICAL PRACTICE

The knowledge that psychological factors are intimately related to the functioning of the uterus is not new. Perhaps recently more objective evidence has been marshalled, but the concept goes back to the Greeks, as the word *hysteria* testifies. As early as the 1920's physicians deplored the fact that fellow physicians were so little interested in the psychogenic causes of female disorders.[5] These self-critical thoughts have appeared again and again in medical literature in the last thirty years.

Yet the present emphasis in gynecology is still overwhelmingly physical. For instance, take the requirement for training as approved by the American Board of Obstetrics and Gynecology—standards the best trained gynecological specialists are expected to meet today in the United States. Some of the requirements are as follows:

Basic science training should emphasize the relation of the basic sciences —anatomy, pathology, physiology, biochemistry and bacteriology—to the application of surgical principles which are fundamental in all branches of surgery. More especially for this specialty there should be training in infertility, endocrinology, oncology, irradiation therapy, electrotherapy, psychosomatic medicine and other nonoperative methods of diagnosis and treatment.[11]

Notice that there is no mention of psychology or psychiatry and only cursory mention of psychosomatic medicine.

In spite of this intensive formal emphasis on the physical, almost every gynecologist is well aware that many of his patients have emotional involvements. It is common to find among gynecologists a great sensitivity to women's feelings of a type that is rare among men of the general population.

Why, then, this lethargy in applying ideas to practice? Partly, of course, there may be the influence of habit and convention and the need for acceptance by colleagues. But is not the main hesitancy due to unfamiliarity with psychological techniques as compared with skill in using physical techniques? When a woman comes seeking help, is it not the most natural thing to help her by using those techniques with which one is most familiar—and using those one knows little about only as a last resort?

It may be argued that psychotherapy is the role of the psychiatrist rather than the gynecologist—and certainly for really disturbed persons this is undoubtedly true. But mind and body are related not only in extreme cases, but in all women. It is here that the physician can be of great help.

PSYCHOLOGICAL TECHNIQUES AND MENSTRUAL DISORDERS

The woman with a fairly well balanced personality who is temporarily disturbed by some very upsetting experience or mode of life can often be helped by sympathetically drawing her out about her troubles and anxieties. Helping her to realize that her amenorrhea or excessive bleeding or pain have occurred subsequent to a set of disturbing circumstances may help her gain insight into their cause.

Questions like "When did the pain first occur?" and "How long does it last?" are, of course, important. But equally important may be the questions like "Do you remember having any particular upsets or worries about the time you first started having the pain?" "Do you find the pain is worse some periods than others?" "What sort of things seem to make it worse?" "Do you find it gets worse when you have been upset about something?" "Tell me about the first time you menstruated when you were 12 years old. How did you and your mother feel about the menstruation then?"

Such questions will, of course, not usually yield immediate or obvious answers to the problem. They will, however, often start physician and patient thinking together along fruitful psychological lines. It goes without saying that such questions can only be fruitful when the physician has established a warm and friendly relationship with the patient.

NEED FOR PSYCHOLOGISTS TO STUDY FEELINGS TOWARD MENSTRUATION

Physicians are fortunate in that it is easier for them to get women talking about menstruation than it is for the psychologist—who has no equal dispensation from the taboos of our society. In our culture there is a great hesitancy for women to discuss menstruation with men. A woman who can talk freely about intercourse to a psychologist or male companion may blush at the very thought of discussing menstruation with these same men.

The result of this is that menstruation is often ignored in considering the personality and adjustment problems of women. Attitude toward intercourse and sexual experience is usually considered an important point to be included in almost any extensive psychological case report; yet seldom are feelings toward menstruation and menstrual experiences even mentioned.

Feelings toward menstruation may be important not only in themselves, but also they may furnish a useful key to understanding the total personality. In the women studied in this research motherly feelings and feelings toward masculinity were found to be related to feelings about menstruation. Surely such emotions toward men and toward children are of basic importance in considering the ability of a woman to lead a happy, well-adjusted life.

SUMMARY

1. The group of women who complained about menstruation were compared with the group of women who did not mind menstruation. Statistical analysis showed twelve specific differences between these two groups.

2. These differences, in general, indicated that the women who were negative toward menstruation were more likely to esteem masculinity, to be unmotherly, and to have gynecological and obstetrical problems. The women who felt positively toward menstruation were more likely to wish for girl babies, to be motherly, to have no menstrual pain, and to have no difficulties bearing children.

3. These findings are understandable in the light of many other research findings which indicate that women's feelings are closely related to the physical course of the menstrual cycle and, conversely, that the menstrual cycle is closely related to women's feelings.

4. Physicians, psychologists, and others who need to understand women should not ignore women's feelings toward their menstrual functions. Feelings toward menstruation may be one key to understanding the whole person and her physical and emotional problems.

REFERENCES

1. ALLEN, E. B. Menstrual dysfunctions in disorders of the personality: Their nature and treatment. *Endocrinology 19:*255, 1935.
2. BENEDEK, THERESE, and RUBENSTEIN, B. B. The sexual cycle in women: The relation between ovarian function and psychodynamic processes. *Psychosom. Med. Monogr. 3:* Nos. 1 and 11, 1942.
3. BILLINGS, E. G. The occurrence of cyclic variations in motor activity in relation to the menstrual cycle in the human female. *Bull. Johns Hopkins Hosp. 54:*440, 1934.
4. CUNNINGHAM, R. L. Dysmenorrhea. *West J. Surg. 42:*274, 1934.
5. DUNBAR, H. FLANDERS *Emotions and Bodily Changes.* New York, Columbia Univ. Press, 1935.
6. GILL, M. M. Functional disturbances of menstruation. *Bull. Menninger Clin. 7:*6, 1943.
7. HAMAN, J. O. Pain threshold in dysmenorrhea. *Am. J. Obst. & Gynec. 47:*686, 1944.
8. HEYER, G. R. "Hypnose und Hypnotherapie." In Birnbaum, K. (ed.): *Die psychischen Heilmethoden.* Leipzig, Thieme, 1927 (cited by Dunbar[5]).
9. HUNTER, W. E., and ROLF, B. B. Psychosomatic aspect of dysmenorrhea. *Am. J. Obst. & Gynec. 53:*123, 1947.
10. JOHNSON, G. B. The effects of periodicity on learning to walk a tightwire. *J. Comp. Psychol. 13:*133, 1932.
11. KIRKLIN, B. R. Approved examining boards in medical specialties. *J. A. M. A. 150:*378, 1952.
12. KROGER, W. S., and FREED, S. C. The psychosomatic treatment of functional dysmenorrhea by hypnosis. *Am. J. Obst. & Gynec. 46:*817, 1943.
13. LOESER, A. A. Emotional shock of hormone release and endometrial development. *Lancet 1:*518, 1943.
14. MAZER, C., and ISRAEL, S. L. *Diagnosis and Treatment of Menstrual Disorders and Sterility.* Ed. 3. New York, Paul B. Hoeber, Inc. 1951.
15. McCANCE, R. A., *et. al.* Physical and emotional periodicity in women. *J. Hyg. 37:*571, 1937.
16. MENNINGER, K. A. Psychogenic influences on the appearance of the menstrual period. *Internat. J. Psycho-Analysis 22:*60, 1941.
17. NOVAK, J., and HARNIK, M. Uterusblutungen psychogenen Ursprungs. *Zentralbl. Gynäk. 53:*2976, 1929 (cited by Dunbar[5]).

18. NOVAK, J. and HARNIK, M. Die Psychogene Entstehung der Menstrualkolik und Deren Behandlung. *Ztschr. f. Geburtsh. u Gynäk. 96:*239, 1929 (cited by Gill[6]).

19. ROSE, A. A. Menstrual pain and personal adjustment. *J. Person. 17:* 287, 1949.

20. SMITH, A. J. Menstruation and industrial efficiency. *J. Appl. Psychol. 34:*1 and 148, 1950.

21. SOWTON, S. C. M., and MEYERS, C. S. Ind. Fat. Res. Board Rep. No. 45 London. H. M. Sta. Off. 1928 (cited by McCance, R. A., *et al.*[15]).

22. WHITACRE, F. E., and BARRERA, B. War Amenorrhea. *J. A. M. A. 124:*399, 1944.

23. WITTKOWER, E., and WILSON, A. T. M. Dysmenorrhea and Sterility. *Brit. M. J. 2:*586, 1940.

CHAPTER 4

WOMEN'S FEELINGS
ABOUT PREGNANCY

FINDINGS OF OTHER RESEARCH STUDIES

Research evidence suggests that pregnancy brings with it certain real emotional problems.

NAUSEA AND VOMITING

A frequently reiterated theory is that vomiting of pregnancy is caused by the emotion of dislike of having the baby. Since vomiting sometimes accompanies disagreeable tasks, it is assumed that the mother who vomits feels disgust about her pregnancy.

The facts of vomiting during pregnancy are by no means as unequivocal as the theoretical speculation. Fitzgerald and Webster compared almost 400 cases of serious pernicious vomiting of pregnancy (hyperemesis gravidarum) with the whole clinic group. Although presumably unmarried mothers would have more mixed feelings toward pregnancy, they found unmarried mothers were no more likely to be afflicted than married mothers. Number of pregnancies, age, and race also did not appear to be related to the incidence of pernicious vomiting, although one would expect acceptance of the child to vary with these factors too.

That feelings of rejection of the baby are *not* related to vomiting in pregnancy is suggested in the well-controlled research of Robertson, a medical general practitioner. Statistical analysis of 100 pregnancies indicated that conscious aversion to pregnancy was not related to nausea and vomiting.

The most marked factor that Robertson did find in women with nausea and vomiting was the experience of frequent undesired sexual intercourse and the absence of orgasm. Only 9 per cent of the control group had disturbed sexual function as compared with 58 per cent of those with minor nausea, 76 per cent of those with moderate nausea, and 100 per cent of those with severe nausea.

That unwanted intercourse rather than a frigid personality may be the factor which leads to nausea and vomiting is suggested by the following case of Robertson's. His patient was a frigid woman who had had seven pregnancies during which she experienced nausea and vomiting. Her husband in the meantime had become a promiscuous drunkard. After the seventh child he contracted syphilis and became separated from his wife. However, he broke into the house to cause the conception of children eight, nine, ten, and eleven. A neighbor as well as the woman herself testified that he made only one visit to start each child. These last four pregnancies, during which time the woman was free from unwanted intercourse, resulted in *no* nausea or vomiting although she had had it with the other seven children.

Pregnant women who consulted their mothers on every decision of importance also were found by Robertson to have a high incidence of nausea and vomiting. Nine per cent of the control group showed this excessive dependence as compared with 19 per cent of the minor nausea group, 47 per cent of the moderate nausea group, and 67 per cent of the severe nausea group.

The changeability of these factors is also emphasized by Robertson. He found that disturbed sexual function, dependence on the mother, and vomiting can change from pregnancy to pregnancy in the same women. Furthermore, he found that simple discussion about the cause of vomiting and nausea successfully alleviated these symptoms in some women.

Further evidence that nausea and vomiting in pregnancy are closely related to mental factors comes from hypnosis and from the study of women of another cultural heritage. Kroger and DeLee report that of 19 cases not cured by other methods, 17 were cured by suggestions under hypnosis with or without hypnoanalysis and age regression. A study of 475 pregnancies of American Indian women[4] done by a physician who cared for them indicates that only 14 per cent of the group had nausea and vomiting. Almost all of those who did have nausea and vomiting were in the group who spoke English. Further evidence of the easy functioning of the reproductive systems of these Indian women comes from the fact that their language had no words for "morning sickness" but has a separate word designating "painless labor."

WORRIES AND DISLIKE OF IDEA OF HAVING A CHILD

Pregnancy for many women in our culture is a period of strain and readjustment. Seventy-five per cent of the normal pregnant women reported on by Hirst and Strousse stated they had more anxiety during pregnancy than before. Wholehearted desire for the baby is by no means universal. Three studies on clinic groups indicate the opposite may be true. Reed reports asking women in a prenatal clinic: "Are you glad you are going to have a baby?" Of 87 women 65 gave negative replies.

However, as pregnancy proceeds attitudes change and become more accepting in most women, according to some accounts. Hall and Mohr found in a study of 66 women that only a few liked the idea of the baby immediately, and a few never liked the idea, but almost two thirds of the women first had a negative reaction and then became reconciled. Thompson, who reports studying 100 women through psychiatric interviews and observation, also found this growing acceptance of the baby as pregnancy progressed. Even the unmarried mothers tended to grow acceptant so that in the end only 5 out of 14 found the baby completely unacceptable.

Hirst and Strousse studied the anxieties of 100 normal pregnant women. Only 16 per cent of the women expressed anxieties about the possible death, ill health, or defectiveness of the baby. Seventeen per cent expressed anxiety about their husbands or other family members. However, 75 per cent appeared to be worried about matters of economic security. Perhaps this dominant anxiety about economic security is a reflection of the pregnant woman's increasing physical dependence on others, and the feelings this dependence engenders in her. Hirst and Strousse found that 80 per cent of the mothers for whom adequate follow-up data were available showed a lessening of anxiety after childbirth even though their economic situation was unchanged.

RESULTS OF THIS STUDY

Previous research suggests that pregnancy may upset the emotions and that emotions may somewhat influence the physical course of pregnancy. This research study concentrates on feelings about pregnancy itself.

Women were considered to have negative feelings about pregnancy if they had unpleasant things to say about pregnancy. They complained about pregnancy, using phrases like "not too good," "all right but. . . ." Some made extreme statements like "miserable" or "sick all the time."

Women were considered to have positive feelings about pregnancy if they did not complain about pregnancy. When they spoke about pregnancy they used such terms as "pretty good," "no trouble," or even sometimes used such words as "wonderful," "swell," "real well."

Women with negative feelings toward pregnancy were found to differ from women with positive feelings toward pregnancy in nine different ways.

These differences are summarized in the following paragraphs. Statistical calculations show that all these differences are quite unlikely to have occurred by chance ($p < 0.2$). The ones that are very unlikely to have occurred by chance ($p < 0.05$) have an asterisk beside them. The statistical details can be found in Appendix D.

The wish to be a man was related to feelings toward pregnancy. Women who liked pregnancy seldom wished to be men, while those who disliked pregnancy more often said they wished to be men.*

Motherly desires were somewhat related to feelings about pregnancy. Women who had negative feelings toward pregnancy were more likely to complain about rooming-in care of their babies and were more apt to be completely unreconciled to the sex of their baby. In spite of the fact that they were older than the positive group,* the negative group had produced no more children. The negative group also were slightly more apt to say that the ideal family is the small family.

Childbirth was related to feelings toward pregnancy. The termination of the disliked pregnancy through the birth process tended to occur quite easily. Women who disliked pregnancy had more normal childbirths* and slightly less frequently had analgesia or anesthesia. Their children tended to gain weight more rapidly after birth.

As might be expected, *economic factors* were related to the attitude toward pregnancy. The highest income group was the most accepting toward pregnancy.

PRACTICAL APPLICATIONS

INADEQUACY OF PRESENT KNOWLEDGE ABOUT PREGNANCY

The average American woman spends more than two years of her life being pregnant.[9] Considering the prevalence of the pregnant state there have been remarkably few objective, well-controlled psychological studies on pregnancy. However, there is a rapidly growing interest in the field which should greatly increase our knowledge in the next few years.

SOME HELPFUL PSYCHOLOGICAL TECHNIQUES IN PREGNANCY

At present a pregnant woman may be helped by applying the few suggestive insights we do have. They can be encouraged to talk about how they actually feel about pregnancy and the idea of having a baby. "How do you like the idea of being pregnant?" or "Are you kind of glad or kind of sorry you are going to have a baby?" may be all that is necessary to start a normal woman expressing her mixed feelings about pregnancy. The second prenatal visit to the physician may be an opportune time for such discussions since it may take some time after the diagnosis of pregnancy before the full emotional impact develops.

Once doubtful feelings are voiced, reassurance can be given by pointing out (1) that unhappiness during the first months of pregnancy is a usual occurrence, and (2) that most women find themselves eager for the baby before it actually arrives despite their earlier feelings. Even financial anxieties tend to disappear after the birth of the baby even if there is no more money.

Problems of nausea and vomiting may be helped by calling attention to the possible causes. Is the woman particularly nauseated the day after having intercourse with her husband? Is she more prone to vomit when she has been in close touch with her mother?

If pregnancy continues to seem hard, thinking together with a pregnant woman along the following lines might be helpful: "How does she feel about becoming a mother?" "Does being a mother mean something nice or something rather disagreeable to her?" "How does she feel about her own mother?" "Has she ever wished to be a man?" "If so, might not this feeling in some ways be related to the feeling that pregnancy is awful?" "Does she feel a little helpless and dependent and does she resent this feeling?"

Such a series of direct questions sprung at a woman one after another would, of course, *not* be helpful. The pregnant woman first needs to feel that the person she is talking to is deeply interested in how she feels and will continue to think well of her regardless of what she says. Under these circumstances an appropriate question or two may help to lead her thinking along surprisingly fruitful lines. To spend a few minutes in such discussion is to recognize the obvious fact that the average normal woman experiences pregnancy *emotionally* as well as *physically,* and needs watching and perhaps a little help in both areas.

SUMMARY

1. The group of women who complained about pregnancy were compared with the group of women who felt fine about pregnancy. Statistical analysis showed nine specific differences between these two groups.

2. These differences, in general, indicated that women who were negative toward pregnancy were more likely to wish to be men and were apt to have fewer motherly desires. Women who were positive toward pregnancy were more apt to be motherly and were less likely to wish to be men. It was the women who were negative toward pregnancy who were most likely to terminate their pregnancies with easy childbirths.

3. Other research studies suggest that feelings about pregnancy may change from rejection to acceptance as pregnancy progresses, and that feelings of nausea during pregnancy may be related to undesired sexual experiences and excessive dependence on the mother.

4. There is great need for more research on the emotions of pregnancy. Meanwhile, it may help to remember that most women experience pregnancy emotionally as well as physically, and need watching and perhaps a little help in both areas.

REFERENCES

1. FITZGERALD, J. E., and WEBSTER, AUGUSTA Hyperemesis gravidarum. *Am. J. Obst. & Gynec. 36:*460, 1938.
2. HALL, D. E., and MOHR, G. J. Prenatal attitudes of primiparae. *Ment. Hyg. 17:*226, 1933.
3. HIRST, J. C., and STROUSSE, FLORA The origin of emotional factors in normal pregnant women. *Am. J. M. Sc. 196:*95, 1938.
4. McCAMMON, C. S. A study of four hundred seventy-five pregnancies in American Indian women. *Am. J. Obst. & Gynec. 61:*1159, 1951.
5. KROGER, W. S., and DeLEE, S. T. The psychosomatic treatment of hyperemesis gravidarum by hypnosis. *Am. J. Obst. & Gynec. 51:*544, 1946.
6. REED, RUTH Changing conception of the maternal instinct. *J Abnorm. & Social Psychol. 18:*78, 1923.
7. ROBERTSON, G. G. Nausea and vomiting in pregnancy. *Lancet 2:*336, 1946.
8. THOMPSON, L. J. Attitudes of primiparae as observed in a prenatal clinic. *Ment. Hyg. 26:*243, 1942.
9. UNITED STATES BUREAU OF CENSUS *Statistical Abstract of the United States,* 1952 (ed. 73). Washington, D. C., Government Printing Office, 1952.

CHAPTER 5

WOMEN'S FEELINGS
ABOUT CHILDBIRTH

FINDINGS OF OTHER RESEARCH STUDIES

Research evidence indicates that childbirth can have an extreme effect on the feelings and emotions of women. Furthermore, there is now considerable evidence showing that the management of feelings toward childbirth influences the nature of the labor and the need for pain relief.

EXTREME EFFECT OF CHILDBIRTH ON SOME WOMEN

Feelings about birth have long been recognized as important factors in the lives of some women. Jeffcoate reported: "The harrowing experience of labour complicated by severe inertia and incoordinate action is a serious deterrent to further childbearing and about one-third of the women or their husbands deliberately avoid further pregnancies. Their decision in this respect is governed mainly by the outcome for the child, and if it survives then . . . they tend to rest content. If, however, the baby is born dead then the natural urge is usually strong enough to overcome the dread of another labour."[13] Jeffcoate reached these conclusions after making a detailed follow-up study of a series of severe inertia cases.[12]

The birth experience is frequently reported as a precipitating factor in mental disorders. Five to 8.7 per cent of the female admissions to mental hospitals are for psychoses following childbirth.[10] However, an extensive statistical study indicates that personality, heredity, and environmental factors may be of great importance in the development of these psychoses although the psychological experiences of childbirth are also implicated.[10]

A THEORY ABOUT THE CAUSE OF NEGATIVE FEELINGS TOWARD BIRTH

In order to review the experimental research on the feelings toward birth and their effect on labor, it is necessary to discuss the general theory and methods used by those who emphasize psychological factors in labor.

The theory was well expressed by Dershimer in 1936. He mentions that Cannon's work shows how emotions affect unstriped muscles, the type found in the uterus, and then states: "All other physiological functions such as eating, coitus, defecation and so on are naturally pleasant and easy. . . . The usual ease with which they naturally occur may be completely destroyed by the development in the individual of certain emotional attitudes in connection with them. Analogy suggests that labor should be naturally pleasant and easy and, when it is not, the common cause of a similar state affecting other functions should be taken as the most likely cause until proved otherwise."

Furthermore he points out: "Society in general makes every possible effort to prevent the pregnant woman from accepting pregnancy and labor as a natural physiologic function. The same amount of attention to eating would make most of us have nervous indigestion."

A TECHNIQUE FOR OVERCOMING NEGATIVE FEELINGS TOWARD BIRTH

Based on this theory that negative feelings in childbirth are largely of psychological and social origin, a new technique was developed to attempt to minimize these causes of pain. The chief inventor and proponent of this technique is Grantly Dick Read.

It involves the following points:

1. Encouraging optimum health in pregnancy through teaching the hygiene of pregnancy with particular emphasis on diet and exercise.

2. Preparing the mother for the sensations and experiences of birth by teaching her the physiology and psychology of labor and familiarizing her with the hospital routines she will be likely to encounter.

3. Psychophysical education with particular emphasis on:
   a. Techniques of physical relaxation so that relaxation is possible despite disturbing experiences.

    b. Control of the muscles around the perineum so that they can be relaxed voluntarily.

    c. Controlled breathing of types that will facilitate relaxation and the efficient and controlled expulsion of the baby.

    d. Practice in spreading the legs wide apart in a way that is necessary for birth so that this can be done easily and without embarrassment.

4. Securing the woman's full cooperation during labor. Explaining to her what is happening and why certain measures are necessary. Giving her repeated encouragement and reassurance.

5. Skilled attendance continually throughout labor by someone the patient has previously known and in whom she has confidence.

6. Emotional support from a beloved member of her family—preferably husband. Beloved individual stays with woman throughout labor.

7. Encouraging mothers to assume positions in labor that are most comfortable to them. This is often a semisquatting position in second stage of labor and a sprawled sideways position for first stage of labor.

8. Careful avoidance of adverse suggestions to patient both before and during labor.
Avoiding unnecessary examinations and manipulation of the patient which might disturb her relaxation.

9. Pleasant, unfrightening surroundings during labor.

10. Anesthesia and analgesia *only* when mother is willing to have it and clinical indications for its use are present, *or* when unusual abnormal circumstances make it imperative. Mother must know that she can have pain relief when she wants it.

OBJECTIVE EVALUATION OF COOPERATIVE PSYCHOLOGICAL TECHNIQUES IN OBSTETRICS

Objective evaluation of this cooperative childbirth* method is difficult to secure. There is a tendency to judge the method after having studied only a few cases or after having applied only part of the method.

---

* Cooperative childbirth is often miscalled "natural childbirth." The essence of the method is the education and emotional support of the mother so that she can cooperate with the physical forces of labor. The method—to be successful—usually also requires a cooperative attitude in the physician, the husband, the prenatal instructor, and the hospital personnel.

Actually it may take considerable time and effort to develop skill in handling cooperative childbirth successfully. Miller[17] found that the primiparas he delivered during the first three months he was using cooperative childbirth methods averaged eleven hours in labor, whereas later they averaged a little over nine hours even when the first cases were included. Unless there is cooperation between hospital, physician, and prenatal class instructor the cooperative childbirth method cannot be given a thorough trial, for only a few portions of the ten-point program can then be used. Published accounts that are based on only a few cases, that are unspecific as to which of the points were used, or that frankly stated that only a small part of the method was used report poor to moderate results.[4,5,9,11,15,23]

Three large series of cases where every effort was made to apply most of the ten points of psychological management give evidence of considerable success. Read[20] reports on 516 consecutive labors. Sixty-four per cent of his mothers needed no pain-relieving measures whatsoever.* In the Yale clinic[26] report on 1000 cases no drug medication (analgesia) was needed by 19 per cent of the primiparas and 48 per cent of the multiparas for vaginal deliveries. Thirty-one per cent of the primiparas and 45 per cent of the multiparas needed no inhalation or conduction block anesthesia. Although the figures for total absence of anesthesia and analgesia are lower than Read's, the great majority of the Yale cases went through labor with no more than 125 mg. demerol and gas given intermittently with contractions.

From the point of view of judging the general applicability of psychological methods, the work of Miller is perhaps the most significance. Working in the small city of Cedar Rapids, Iowa, he decided to apply cooperative childbirth theories to his own practice. He did so with such thoroughness that he not only provided classes for all his patients and their husbands, but also had the nurse instructor of these courses give emotional support during labor. The fame of the Yale clinic and of Read is such that they soon attracted women rather atypical of the general population. Miller's series does not seem to have suffered from this type of distortion of sampling to a great extent.

Miller reports on 585 consecutive cases.[17] Ninety-five per cent of these women were able to have spontaneous vaginal deliveries. Of these, 81 per cent of his multiparas and 47 per cent of his primiparas needed only 50 mg. of demerol or less.† Ninety-six per cent of the multiparas

* Fourteen per cent of these did have barbiturate or chloral and bromide to induce sleep in early labor at night.

† A single dose of demerol is usually about 100 mg. and in conventional deliveries women quite often get a total of 200 mg. or more.

and 93 per cent of the primiparas needed only whiffs of nitrous oxide or none at all. All these mothers were conscious at all times and heard the baby's first cry.*

HYPNOSIS *Versus* OTHER PSYCHOLOGICAL METHODS

It has been suggested that the success of cooperative childbirth methods is due to their hypnotic effect. Both hypnosis and cooperative childbirth methods depend on *suggestion* to some extent, but they are not one and the same thing. Lorand, in an experimental study of 26 cases, found that the feeling of fear and pain of childbirth can only be completely obliviated with such deep hypnosis that it automatically causes amnesia. In contrast to this, cooperative childbirth mothers at Yale[8] had surprisingly accurate memories of birth. Mothers were asked to give in detail accounts of their birth experience two or three times at different intervals after birth. Their accounts were correlated with those of the attending doctor and nurse. The correlations were substantial and no large gaps in memory were found.

Some of the confusion of thinking may be due to the fact that the line between *light* hypnosis and other psychological methods is a thin one. Undoubtedly the repeated suggestion in reading and in class work that labor need not be unduly painful actually makes it less painful. This is merely the reverse of the usual effect of our culture which constantly suggests that childbirth is torture.

Although only about 20 per cent of individuals are capable of deep pain-obliterating hypnosis, Abramson points out that even light hypnosis heightens the relaxation and suggestibility of the patient. The 100 women he prepared during pregnancy by hypnotic sessions on the average definitely had shorter first stages of labor than a control group. This difference was statistically significant. Abramson feels that his results would have been even better if his patients had not been exposed to the screaming of other patients, and had the nurses spoken to them in pleasant, calm voices and explained to them what was going to happen to them before initiating disturbing medical procedures. These are just the points cooperative childbirth advocates emphasize.

RESULTS OF THIS STUDY

Other research shows that the experience of childbirth can have great emotional impact, and that psychological influences can affect

* More than twice as many primiparas as multiparas wanted no gas at all. Miller remarks on this: "We believe that this is due to the fact that the multiparas have had anesthetics in previous deliveries, and consider it a necessity."[17]

the experiences of labor. This research concentrates on women's emotions toward childbirth and how these emotions are related to other aspects of their lives.

Women were considered to have negative feelings toward birth if they said unpleasant things about childbirth. The least extreme ones spoke of childbirth as being "a little hard" or "not so easy"; while the most extreme ones used such words as "terrible," "awful," or emphasized their accounts of their suffering with swear words.

Women were considered to have positive feelings toward birth if they said childbirth was "easy" or "pretty good" or "very easy."

The range of feeling expressed by the mothers about childbirth was tremendous. The same question elicited replies like:

"Good God—did I have a hard time! It could have killed me!"

"I don't think I could stand it again. I said: 'Take away the baby. I don't want to see it.' "

"I thought she were about 12 to 15 pounds. It was awful! It was horrible!"

And replies like:

"I didn't have such a hard time. I had more pain carrying it than I did birthing it."

"I had six hard pains and there she was!"

"I had an easy time. She was born on a stretcher. I didn't have no more than four real hard pains."

Women with negative feelings about childbirth were found to be different from women with positive feelings about childbirth in six different ways.

These differences are summarized in the following paragraphs. Statistical calculations show that all of these differences are quite unlikely to have occurred by chance ($p<0.2$). The ones that are very unlikely to have occurred by chance ($p<0.05$) have an asterisk beside them. The statistical details can be found in Appendix D.

The physical expression of affection for the baby was related to feelings about birth. Breast feeding and rooming-in were more popular with mothers who had positive feelings about birth. It was the mothers who felt birth was hard who were more likely to want to formula feed their infants.* It was also these women with negative feelings toward birth who were most likely to complain about having to take care of their babies.*

Social and physical factors were also related to feelings about birth. Mothers who felt negative about birth had had fewer children,* and had fewer completely normal births. Women from the semiskilled groups reported more positive feelings toward birth than the women from the lower or higher income-occupation groups.

Analgesia and anesthesia were somewhat related to feelings about birth in the opposite way than is commonly expected. Women who had received *no* general anesthesia or analgesia were slightly more likely to have positive feelings toward birth than those who had been drugged.

PRACTICAL APPLICATIONS

NEED FOR PAIN RELIEF IN LABOR

Childbirth can be one of the most excruciatingly painful experiences any human being can suffer. Pain as measured by the thermal radiation method is reported in some women to reach 10 to 10½ dols.[11] This degree of pain is the most extreme pain human beings are capable of feeling and is comparable to the pain felt in extreme forms of physical torture or third-degree burns.

In this research the mothers who felt birth was hard were more likely to want their babies fed by bottle and cared for in the nursery. Women who had positive feelings about birth also were apt to want to breast feed and to look after their babies themselves. This contrast between women who felt childbirth hard and those who felt it easy was one of the strongest contrasts found in this whole research study. Similar evidence comes from Jeffcoate's finding that women who had labors characterized by uterine inertia often refused to have another child. The fact that psychoses are precipitated by childbirth gives further indication that childbirth is a very potent experience.

TWO METHODS OF DEALING WITH PAIN IN LABOR

There is general agreement that the pain of childbirth may have such extreme repercussions that something should be done about it. There are only two ways to deal with the problem. One is to give symptomatic relief and the other is to eliminate the cause of the pain.

Those who believe that the pain of labor is inevitable and inherent in the process of childbearing are inclined to use symptomatic relief. They depend chiefly on pharmacological methods of pain control. Those who believe the cause of pain in normal labor is largely social and psychological naturally tend to emphasize measures of psychological support and re-education.

DIFFICULTIES OF USING PHARMACOLOGICAL METHODS OF PAIN CONTROL

The possibility of a normal delivery is virtually eliminated when complete general or spinal anesthesia is given. Thoms and Wyatt in a large series of cases found that the number of instrumental vaginal deliveries increased in direct proportion to the amount of pharmacological pain relief administered. Ninety-eight per cent of women having no inhalation or spinal anesthesia delivered spontaneously as compared with only 20 per cent of women who had complete inhalation or spinal anesthesia.

Even sedation during the early stages of labor was found to have a deleterious effect on the eventual outcome of labor. Women who had no drug medication were able to deliver their own babies 97 per cent of the time. Women who had three doses of drug medication delivered spontaneously only 69 per cent of the time.

As far as the baby is concerned, the exact figures on asphyxia do not seem to be available. However, in some hospitals where heavy sedation and anesthesia are routine about one in six babies may need active measures of resuscitation, and almost every baby is given oxygen at birth. In a report of almost six hundred cases in which primarily psychological methods of pain control were used, none of the babies needed resuscitation, although a few were put in an air lock for removal of excess mucus.

Another possible disadvantage of anesthesia and analgesia is that they may not actually be as effective in mitigating negative feelings as is often assumed. Read[21] points out that anesthesia and analgesia dull the joy that often comes after the hard work of producing the baby. Such women remember the pain experienced before sedation, but fail to have the compensation of elation that often accompanies being awake for the arrival of a beloved baby.

The result of this research is in line with his theory. The women who *had* general anesthesia and/or analgesia had slightly *more* negative feelings toward birth.

Read[21] also suggests that unconscious delivery may dull mother love itself. The results of this research show that women who were given pharmacological measures of pain relief had somewhat different attitudes toward several major aspects of their lives.

It was the mothers who were given pharmacological measures of pain relief who were a little more likely to show negative feelings toward menstruation and baby care, and who were slightly more likely to feel that men had the most satisfying time in life. They looked back on their pregnancies in slightly more positive terms. Mothers who had no drugs or anesthesia of any sort except for a little local injection of procain were the mothers who were slightly more likely to feel that women had a satisfying time in life. They also voiced positive feelings about menstruation and child care a little more frequently, but had slightly more negative feelings about pregnancy.

These facts lead to the suggestion that women who have positive feelings toward some parts of their biologically determined role may have less need for pharmacological measures of pain relief. On the other hand it might also be true that rendering a woman insensitive or unconscious during such an important event in her life sometimes has severe psychological repercussions.

DIFFICULTIES IN USING PSYCHOLOGICAL METHODS OF PAIN CONTROL

One of the difficulties in applying psychological measures to control pain is the widespread impression among women that cooperative childbirth is more painful childbirth. They do not realize that cooperative childbirth actually is childbirth so regulated that the need for pain relief is greatly minimized, and that pain relief is immediately given when desired. Most women would probably be wholeheartedly for most of the ten points (see pages 31 and 32) involved in cooperative childbirth if they had a chance to choose them. Few, indeed, would be against the idea of never being left alone in labor or against similar comforting measures.

Although physicians, too, are inclined to favor most of the ten points of cooperative childbirth as "ideal," there are practical, financial, and psychological difficulties involved in its application. Hospital rules intervene. The excess time consumed means limiting practice or using the services of a nurse to give emotional support during labor. There is less opportunity to use the operative type of obstetrical skills which were learned through hard and expensive years of training. The close relationship between obstetrician and patient has to be shared with a husband or other beloved member of the patient's family. The patient herself, as she becomes educated in the physiology of childbirth, may become assertive in demanding that childbirth be managed according to her own particular inclinations.

The degree to which physicians welcome cooperative childbirth depends on the whole attitude of the society in which they live. In Sweden[2] all normal deliveries both in the hospital and at home are done by women especially trained in obstetrics for about two years. However, the administration of anesthesia is often considered serious enough to merit a doctor's attention. Needless to say, Read's theories of cooperative childbirth were favorably accepted by Swedish physicians in general.

Certain portions of the Read program have crossed the Atlantic more easily than others. Education for childbirth and the management of the first stage of labor have generally been more or less adopted by the cooperative childbirth advocates in this country. However, even the most enthusiastic physicians in this country seem to place much less emphasis on breast feeding and a normal second stage of labor. Read makes a point of mentioning that 98 per cent of his mothers were breast feeding their babies on leaving the hospital.[20] Americans publishing similar articles usually do not feel breast feeding is enough of a parturient process to publish statistics on it along with childbirth statistics.

DIFFERENCES IN MANAGEMENT OF SECOND STAGE OF LABOR

The most interesting cultural difference, however, comes in the management of the second stage of labor. When delivery seems imminent the American woman is suddenly transported from her bed, pushed into a room with brilliant lights and medical instruments. She is then put on a special table that has equipment for tying her hands and feet, and her buttocks are so adjusted that she pushes her baby out into space, with no mattress to break its fall should the doctor fail to catch it. Labor is then quite usually artificially shortened by cutting the woman's perineum.

In contrast to this, Read's patients are not routinely hauled into a frightening new environment just as the baby is about to emerge. Read advocates a much more leisurely second stage of labor. Miller's normal primiparas spent an average of 35 minutes in the second stage of labor.[17] The comparable figure at Yale was 51 minutes.[26] Read thinks that even an hour in second stage is undesirably short.[21] His primiparas averaged an hour and 25 minutes.[20]

The results of the two methods of handling the second stage of labor may be seen in the statistics:

79 per cent of Read's primiparas had intact perineums or just abrasions (first-degree tears)

10 per cent of Miller's primiparas had their birth passages left in a similarly normal condition

13 per cent of Yale* primiparas did not have cut perineums (no episiotomies)

The similar figures for multiparas are 96 per cent for Read, 55 per cent for Miller, and 78 per cent for Yale.*

* The Yale percentages represent those who had no episiotomies. Presumably some of these women had tears and abrasions.

Read[19] states that in over 90 per cent of uncomplicated births his patients refused analgesia or anesthetic, whereas the great majority of cooperative childbirth mothers in this country get whiffs of gas as well as local sensation-deadening agents like procain.

One of the largest differences between the writings of Read and the writings of the men on this side of the Atlantic is that he speaks repeatedly of the overwhelming joy the mothers find in producing their babies at the end of the second stage of labor. Much less is made of this joy in the reports on this side of the Atlantic. Is it possible that the different management of the second stage of labor has something to do with this?

SUMMARY

1. The group of women who felt that childbirth was hard were compared with the group of women who felt childbirth was easy. Statistical analysis showed six specific differences between these two groups.

2. These differences, in general, indicated that women who felt negatively about birth were more likely to be physically less motherly women. They had fewer children, and were more likely to dislike breast feeding and rooming-in care of their babies. Women who felt positively about birth, on the other hand, were more apt to want to breast feed and almost always enjoyed the rooming-in care of their babies. They had more babies.

3. Other research shows that the experiences of childbirth sometimes cause severe emotional trauma and conversely that psychological influences can affect the experiences of labor.

4. Pharmacological methods of pain control lead to instrumental deliveries and infants who may have difficulty breathing at first. Furthermore, this research suggests the possibility that it is women who are rendered insensitive or unconscious during labor who are more likely to harbor negative feelings about childbirth and some other aspects of their womanly role.

5. Cooperative, psychological methods of pain control are effective in minimizing and often eliminating the need for anesthesia and analgesia during labor. These methods are desirable since they emphasize the need for considerate treatment and continuous emotional support of the parturient woman.

REFERENCES

1. ABRAMSON, M., and HERON, W. T. An objective evaluation of hypnosis in obstetrics. *Am. J. Obst. & Gynec. 59:*1069, 1950.
2. ANDERSON, ASTRID Midwife practice in Sweden. *Transactions of the Fifth American Congress of Obstetrics and Gynecology* St. Louis, Mo., Mosby, 1952.
3. BOWERS, P. A. Husbands in the delivery room. *Child-Family Digest 6:*3, April, 1952.
4. CALLAHAN, J. T. A physician's viewpoint on preparation for childbirth. *Transactions of the Fifth American Congress on Obstetrics and Gynecology* St Louis, Mo., Mosby, 1952.
5. DAVIDSON, H. B. The psychosomatic aspects of educated childbirth. *New York State J. Med. 53:*2499, 1953.
6. DERSHIMER, F. W. The influence of mental attitudes in childbearing. *Am. J. Obst. & Gynec. 31:*444, 1936.
7. GOODRICH, F. W. *Natural Childbirth.* New York, Prentice-Hall, 1950.
8. FREEDMAN, L. Z. *et al.* Training for childbirth: Remembrance of labor. *Psychosom. Med. 14:*439, 1952.
9. HEARDMAN, HELEN *A Way to Natural Childbirth.* Edinburgh, Livingstone, 1951.
10. JACOBS, BETTY Aetiological factors and reaction types in psychoses following childbirth. *J. Ment. Sc. 89:*242, 1943.
11. JAVERT, C. T., and HARDY, J. D. Measurement of pain intensity in labor and its physiologic, neurologic and pharmacologic implications. *Am. J. Obst. & Gynec. 60:*552, 1950.
12. JEFFCOATE, T. N. A. Inco-ordinate uterine action in labour. *Trans. Edinburgh Obst. Soc. 101:*23, 1949.
13. JEFFCOATE, T. N. A. In *Modern Trends in Obstetrics and Gynecology.* New York, Hoeber, 1950, p. 246, ed., Kenneth Bowes.
14. LORAND, A. Painless delivery by hypnosis from the neurological standpoint. *Gyógyszerész i hetil,* 1923. (Cited by Freedman. I. Z., et al.[8])
15. MANDY, A. T., *et al.* Is natural childbirth natural? *Psychosom. Med. 14:*431, 1952.
16. MILLER, H. L., *et al.* Education for childbirth in private practice: 450 consecutive cases. *Am J. Obst. & Gynec. 63:*792, 1952.
17. MILLER, H. L., and FLANNERY, F. E. Education for childbirth in private practice: 585 consecutive cases. *Child-Family Digest 6:*33, April, 1952.
18. READ, G. D. *Childbirth Without Fear.* New York, Harper & Brothers, 1944.
19. READ, G. D. The discomforts of childbirth. *Brit. M. J. 1:*651, 1949.
20. READ, G. D. Observations on a series of labors with special reference to physiological delivery. *Lancet 1:*721, 1949.

21. READ, G. D. *The Birth of a Child.* New York, Vanguard, 1950.

22. READ, G. D. *Introduction to Motherhood.* New York, Harper & Brothers, 1950.

23. RODWAY, H. E. A statistical study on the effects of exercises on child-bearing. *J. Obst. & Gynaec. Brit. Emp. 54:*77, 1947.

24. THOMS, H. *Training for Childbirth.* New York, McGraw-Hill, 1950.

25. THOMS, H. in collaboration with ROTH, L. G. *Understanding Natural Childbirth.* New York, McGraw-Hill, 1950.

26. THOMS, H. and WYATT, R. H. One thousand consecutive deliveries under a training for childbirth program. *Am J. Obst. & Gynec. 61:*205, 1951.

CHAPTER 6

WOMEN'S FEELINGS
ABOUT BREAST FEEDING

FINDINGS OF OTHER RESEARCH STUDIES

There is a considerable body of objective evidence that indicates that women's emotions are closely related to the physical course of lactation and that, conversely, the physical course of lactation is closely related to women's emotions.

DESIRE TO BREAST FEED: RELATION TO SUCCESS

The attitude of the mother is an important factor in her breast feeding success. Newton and Newton[28] studied this relationship in detail in a series of 91 mothers. Mothers who wholeheartedly wanted to breast feed were more successful at breast feeding. Significantly more of them had enough milk to make bottle supplementation unnecessary by the fifth day after birth. Specifically:

74 per cent of those who said "I am going to breast feed," "I prefer to breast feed," or who made similar positive statements actually had enough milk.

35 per cent of those who said "I'll give both breast and bottle," "It doesn't matter," or made similar statements showing ambivalence or indifference had enough milk.

26 per cent of those who showed they preferred artificial feeding had enough milk, although they were trying to breast feed.

Mothers who wanted to breast feed actually gave their babies significantly more milk at an average fourth-day feeding:

59 Gm. of milk were given by mothers who wanted to breast feed.

42 Gm. of milk were given by mothers who were half-hearted about breast feeding.

35 Gm. of milk were given by mothers who preferred artificial feeding but who were trying to breast feed.

Reports of the babies' reaction to feeding differed with the mothers' desire to breast feed. As compared with mothers who wanted to breast feed their babies, mothers who preferred artificial feeding were three times as likely to report that their baby refused the breast and were twice as likely to report that the baby had difficulty sucking. On the other hand, mothers who wanted to breast feed more often reported that their babies just refused to take the bottle!

INFLUENCE OF EMOTIONS ON SECRETION OF MILK

Emotions may influence the secretion of milk in several ways. First, they may directly reduce the blood flow through the breast, second, they may reduce sucking which stimulates the secretion of milk, and third, they may lead to performing lactation rituals which interfere with the success of breast feeding.

The reduction of blood flow may be one way in which emotions interfere with the secretion of milk. This is suggested by the work of Petersen[31] who used excised perfused udders. He found that when he circulated the blood of markedly excited cows through these udders, the blood flow was reduced to as little as one-fourth of normal. Since the blood contains the precursors of milk, an ample blood flow is probably an essential prerequisite to an ample milk supply.

Sucking stimulation is of paramount importance in the establishment of an adequate milk supply. It is so important that experimental animals[37] and women in primitive societies[14, 18, 43] can establish an adequate milk supply for adopted babies simply by allowing enough sucking to take place. The woman who is doubtful or negative about breast feeding probably shows her hesitancy by allowing less sucking. Newton and Newton found that women who preferred artificial feeding were twice as likely to use nipple shields while in the hospital, although they had a lower incidence of fissured nipples and therefore less cause for protecting them.[28]

Third, the emotions may lead to the *adoption of lactation rituals* which adversely influence breast feeding. "Nipple care" in our culture is a good example of this. The standard advice to mothers is to keep their nipples clean. Nipples in our society are well protected by clothing from outside soil so that the "dirt" mothers wash off is mostly the natural accumulation of sweat, sebum, and milk.

These nipple secretions are probably very important to the health of the nipple skin by preparing it to withstand vigorous sucking.[24] Sweat with sebum has antibacterial properties. Sebum is an important contributor to the protective covering of the skin, and helps to keep the skin pliable. Sweat may also help to keep the skin pliable and normally acid. The breast milk itself may also contribute to the health of the nipple skin. Newly secreted human milk is very rich in lysozyme—an antibacterial substance.

The result of keeping the nipples "clean" is damaged nipples and excruciating pain in some instances. An experimental study[24] found that mothers washing their nipples with soap solution had more nipple pain on all five days of their hospital stay than the control group who used only water. The pain was both more frequent and more extreme. Nipple pain in turn causes a limitation of sucking and the failure of breast feeding.

Unfortunately, the deep disgust many members of our contemporary society feel toward all body secretions makes rational nipple care difficult. In spite of facts to the contrary, there remains a deep unshaken emotion that a nipple, with its profusion of secretions, must be soaped or otherwise tampered with. Several other lactation rituals are similarly harmful to milk secretion—and similarly, in spite of objective evidence to the contrary, they continue to be practiced. It is emotions rather than intellect that lead to the resulting curtailed secretion of milk.

Influence of Emotions on Expulsion of Milk

There are two major mechanisms involved in breast feeding. One is the secretion of milk; the other is the expulsion of milk. The breast can be distended with milk but if the expulsion mechanism fails, the baby fails to get enough milk.

Another name for the expulsion mechanism is the let-down reflex. A series of experiments by Petersen [9, 31, 32] in cows indicated that sucking stimulation causes the posterior pituitary to discharge oxytocic hormone which acts on the smooth muscle fibers near the alveoli. These contract and thus the milk is pushed out into the larger ducts where it is available to the milking machine. The experiments of Waller and of Newton and Newton[20, 27] have demonstrated that the let-down reflex also exists in human beings.

The importance of this let-down reflex lies in the fact that it is very sensitive to emotions. Good dairymen know that fright, unfamiliar surroundings, or unkind treatment will cause a cow to "refuse" to let down her milk. Ely and Petersen and Newton and Newton[20] have inhibited the reflex experimentally. Ely and Petersen found that a cow with a cat placed on her back gave little milk in spite of the fact that there was a lot in her udder. Newton and Newton found that the baby got significantly less milk when the mother was subjected to pain or emotional disturbance. The amount of milk the baby received returned to normal in spite of the mother's emotional state when oxytocic hormone was injected—thus setting off the reflex artificially.

Breast feeding failure is related to let-down reflex inhibition. Newton and Newton[27] found that women who needed to give their babies supplemental formulas actually keep almost 50 per cent of their milk in their breast. Neither the sucking baby nor the breast pump could remove it. However, it could be removed by setting off the let-down reflex artificially with injections of oxytocic hormone. In a study of 103 nursing mothers,[27] the Newtons found that mothers whose babies did not need supplemental bottles had significantly more symptoms of let-down than mothers who needed to give supplemental feedings. The reflex seemed to work less erratically in the successful mothers for there was significantly less variation in the amount of milk the baby got from one feeding to the next.

BREAST FEEDING AND MATERNAL EMOTIONS

There is some direct evidence that breast feeding and maternal behavior may be related. Freeman, who compared 100 problem children who were breast fed twelve months or longer with 100 problem children who were breast fed one month or less, found marked differences in the maternal attitudes of their mothers. Of those who had little or no breast feeding, 50 per cent were rejected and 19 per cent were overprotected. The opposite ratio was true of those who had had twelve months or more of breast feeding. Forty-nine per cent of these received excessive mothering as compared to 20 per cent who were rejected. Levy, in his study of "excessively" motherly women, found that 50 per cent of them nursed their babies a year or more.

There is some evidence that the lactation hormones present and active throughout the lactation period influence the behavior of the mother. Maternal behavior has been induced in virgin rats by injecting prolactin.[34] A recent article[4] reports the case of a policeman who had a pituitary disorder which caused an increase in the lactogenic pituitary hormone. During the period of his disorder he became very maternal as compared with his previous behavior. When his hormone level returned to normal, his maternal behavior became less marked.

The third type of evidence we have for the relationship between breast feeding and maternal behavior comes from inspecting the size of families. Because there are some very maternal women who have only one or two children and some neglectful mothers who have many children, we are apt to forget what a good general measure of maternal behavior the size of the family actually is. Freeman, in her study of the large group of problem children, found that children with no siblings had less breast feeding than children of larger families. Newton[23] in her small group of normal children found a similar relationship. She found that seven out of ten "first" children had experienced supplemented or successful breast feeding, whereas only one out of nine "only" children had done so. In England the recent extensive national survey[8] found that mothers of four or more children were less apt to try to breast feed; but once breast feeding was established, it continued longer. The average first, second, or third child was weaned slightly earlier than the average fourth or subsequent child. The relationship found in this study between breast feeding attitude and number of children was negligible, probably because it did not measure the average weaning date.

RESULTS OF THIS STUDY

Previous research gives clear evidence that emotions influence breast feeding and that breast feeding is in turn affected by emotions. This research study concentrates on feelings toward breast feeding itself and how these feelings are related to other aspects of the woman's life.

Women were considered to have negative feelings about breast feeding if they said they preferred to use bottles. Some said they planned to start bottles only after a month or two or planned to use the breast milk along with formula. Only a very few were so negative that they refused to breast feed the baby in the hospital.

Women who made unmitigated statements about their desire to breast feed were considered positive toward breast feeding. Some definitely planned to breast feed their babies five months or more while others spoke of breast feeding from two to five months.

Women with negative feelings toward breast feeding were found to differ from women with positive feelings toward breast feeding in eight different ways.

These differences are summarized in the following paragraphs. Statistical calculations show that all of these differences are unlikely to have occurred by chance ($p<0.2$). The ones that are very unlikely to have occurred by chance ($p<0.05$) have an asterisk beside them. The statistical details can be found in Appendix D.

Feelings about woman's role in life were related to feelings about breast feeding. Women who wanted to feed their babies artificially were more likely to feel that childbirth was hard,* and that men had a more satisfying time in life.* Mothers who did not want to nurse their babies were also more apt to complain about looking after their babies in the hospital. Women who were positive toward breast feeding, on the other hand, were more likely to feel childbirth was easy,* that rooming-in baby care was fine, and that women have at least as satisfying a time in life as men.*

Successful breast feeding was related to attitude toward breast feeding. Virtually all of the women were breast feeding at the time they were interviewed. However, mothers who desired to feed artificially were likely to be less successful at breast feeding during their hospital stay. The difference between the positive and negative groups was more pronounced six weeks after birth. Breast feeding without bottle supplementation occurred much more frequently among the mothers who had stated a desire to breast feed.* These findings confirm early work done by Newton and Newton[28] on the same subject.

The reproductive organs and the breast are closely related. The oxytocic hormone causes both uterine contractions and the let-down of milk. In view of this it is interesting to note that primiparas who wanted to breast feed were more likely to have very short labors.* Primiparas who did not want to breast feed were likely to have longer labors.* It has also been suggested that breast feeding has sexual implication. Thus it is interesting to find that boy babies were desired somewhat more often by women who wanted to breast feed than by those who wanted to bottle feed.

Since mothers in the semiskilled occupation income group had the most positive feelings about birth, it is not surprising to find they also had the most positive feelings about breast feeding.

PRACTICAL APPLICATIONS

SOURCES OF MISUNDERSTANDING

There is a great deal of confused thought about breast feeding. A large part of this is due to the undefined use of the term "breast feeding," which can have many different connotations. There are two main types of breast feeding, which for want of better terms will be called successful breast feeding and unsuccessful breast feeding.

Successful breast feeding is the type of feeding that is practiced by the vast majority of mothers all over the world.[25, 26] It is a simple, easy process. When the baby is hungry, it is simply given a breast to suck. There is an abundance of milk, and the milk supply naturally adjusts itself to the child's growth and intake of other foods. It never occurs to the mother to worry about whether the baby is getting enough. The milk is ready and waiting to satisfy the baby's needs. Both mother and baby enjoy the process so much that weaning tends to be postponed rather than hastened.

Unsuccessful breast feeding is a type of breast feeding that is typical of the modern urban American mother. This type of breast feeding is a difficult and tenuous process. There is constant worry about whether there is enough milk for the baby. The mother is expected to regulate her diet, her sleep, and her habits of living to help make her milk good and plentiful. She worries about washing her nipples, and about which breast to give, and when and how long to give it. She often weighs the baby before and after feeding to see whether the baby has got enough, and is advised to express the milk remaining in her breast by hand after each feeding—a laborious process. Often the supply of milk is so insufficient that bottles must be resorted to to supplement the breast milk. Breast abscesses and engorgement, and nipple fissures and erosions frequently cause extreme pain.[21, 22, 24] The pain, the work, and the worry of unsuccessful breast feeding make early weaning part of the unsuccessful breast-feeding pattern.

Naturally, there are many breast feeding situations that are neither one type nor the other but fall between the two. By and large, however, the two types can be clearly differentiated.

Is Breast Feeding Psychologically Desirable?

One of the favorite psychological clichés is that breast feeding makes a child feel "secure." Actually, in terms of objective evidence the psychological advantage of breast feeding is by no means clear.[29, 30]

The findings of Newton's small exploratory study done on normal kindergarten children are typical of the complex picture presented by research investigation.[23] Newton found that children who were breast fed for two or three months with bottle supplementation most of the time (i.e., unsuccessful breast feeding) had the lowest average adjustment and average social adaptability scores. They daydreamed the most and were seldom chosen as playmates. Children whose mothers never tried to breast feed them tended to disturb other children at work and play much more than any of those who had any breast feeding. It was the children who had been successfully breast fed for four to six months, and those who had been breast fed only a week or two, who showed the most desirable behavior. They had the highest average adjustment scores, were the most popular with children, showed the most friendliness toward both children and adults, and took the most responsibility.

Newton's complex findings on the relationship between behavior and breast feeding are in keeping with those of Childers and Hamil, Hoefer and Hardy, Maslow and Szilagyi–Kessler, all of whom have found curvilinear relationships. Both Peterson and Spano and Holway looked only for linear relationships. Holway, working with only 17 children, found high linear correlations; but Peterson and Spano found no significant evidence of such a linear relationship.

More research which considers the whole nature of the breast feeding situation is badly needed. The number of months of breast feeding are probably much less important psychologically than the *type* of breast feeding and the *type* of weaning involved. Was the breast feeding unsuccessful breast feeding—with all the tension, fear, and pain that that involves? Or was it successful breast feeding with its peace of mind and physical pleasure? Was the weaning sudden, or was it so gradual that neither mother nor baby seemed to notice the transition? A successfully breast fed baby who is suddenly weaned may be more psychologically hurt than the artificially fed baby who has never known such close intimacy with another human being.

Since the baby is so young and pliable, the psychological effects of the feeding experience are much more important to him than to his mother. Much of his first knowledge of the world comes through his feeding. Yet it should not be overlooked that artificial feeding has a different effect on the mother as well as the baby, and this in turn affects their whole relationship.

The breast feeding mother is different from the artificially feeding mother in four ways. First of all, Prolactin, which is known to produce maternal behavior in experimental animals,[34] is also presumably present and operative in the breast feeding mother. The fact that maternal behavior can be induced by hormones in human beings is suggested by the case report of the man who became very maternal during a pituitary disorder.[4]

Second, oxytocin is liberated each time the mother lets down her milk. This hormone acts on the uterus as well as the breast. Tests[19] indicate that the uterus contracts rhythmically during breast feeding and for about 20 minutes after the baby stops eating. This generalized effect may be one reason why successful breast feeding gives sensuous enjoyment to the mother. Spence aptly describes this feeling when he speaks of the look of "lascivious content" that comes over some mothers as they nurse their babies.

Third, successful breast feeding gives rise to the gentle and prolonged stroking of one of the most sensitive parts of the female body—the nipple. This in turn involves sensuous pleasure.[25]

Fourth, the breast feeding mother has a real physical need for the baby just as the baby has need of the mother. The mother's breasts become distended with milk, and there is physical relief in having the baby empty them. Too long a gap between feedings leads to discomfort in *both* mother and baby.

It is true, of course, that deep affection characterizes many mothers who bottle feed their babies. However, it is inaccurate to say that the bottle-fed baby who is held and cuddled with each feeding has the same sort of relationship with his mother as the successfully breast-fed baby. Insofar as the mother's whole body as well as the baby's body is involved in breast feeding, the relationship is most definitely *different*.

Is Breast Feeding Physically Desirable?

As compared with artificial feeding, successful breast feeding seems to continue to have certain physical advantages for mother and baby. However, these physical advantages are greatly minimized in unsuccessful breast feeding, since unsuccessful breast feeding often involves early weaning and traumatic breast disorders.

Failure to use the breast for its biological purpose *may predispose to breast cancer*. Women who have never lactated, or who have had lactation disorders, are reported to have a higher rate of breast cancer. In one study[1] done on 200 consecutive breast cancer cases only 8.5 per cent of the women had breast fed children successfully, whereas 62 per cent of the noncancerous controls had done so. In the cancerous group every third pregnancy ended in miscarriage or abortion with the resulting stasis of the breast. In the control group only one in every seven pregnancies had resulted in miscarriage. Recently an extensive French study[6] on women operated on for breast cancer has tended to confirm this American finding.

A pilot study by Bagg on mice suggests that this same phenomenon may occur in animals. Bagg subjected 15 mice to repeated rapid pregnancies with litters removed from their mothers within twelve hours after birth. Thus the breast was repeatedly prepared for lactation, but normal sucking was denied. Thirteen of the 15 mice (87 per cent) developed mammary carcinoma at a comparatively early age. The control group had a tumor incidence of less than 5 per cent and these tumors did not occur until a later age.

Breast feeding may be a *natural form of birth control* or means of spacing children. Series of endometrial biopsies indicate that lactation tends to suppress ovulation.[41] In the British study[8] on a national sample of almost 5000 mothers, it was found that until the baby was nine months old the breast feeding mother had a conception rate of about half that of the formula feeding mother. Once lactation ceased, the fertility rate of these breast feeding mothers rose to that of the rest of the sample. The effect of this is that the average breast-fed child is more likely to get its mother's undivided energies during its early infancy, and that the mother is less likely to be worn out with repeated rapid pregnancies.

Breast feeding may also influence the *development of the baby*. The body composition of the breast-fed baby differs from that of the artificially fed baby.[15] The bottle-fed baby's body retains more nitrogen and calcium. The artificially fed baby after the first few months becomes definitely heavier than the breast-fed infant[8, 10] and this weight difference is maintained for as long as two years.[8] Two studies have found that formula-fed babies walk later than breast-fed infants.[8, 12] This relationship remained even when the heavier weight of the bottle-fed baby is statistically discounted and even when premature and weakly infants, who are more likely to be formula fed, are excluded from the group.[8] Artificially fed babies show less body activity than breast-fed babies. A study of babies[7] in the first ten days of life found that, beginning with the sixth day of life, the breast-fed infants showed slightly but usually significantly more general body activity. The breast-fed babies also developed a stronger sucking reflex than either the bottle- or cup-fed babies.

A huge number of studies have attempted to compare the *health of the breast-fed* and the artificially fed infant. The risks of artificial feeding vary tremendously with the differences in environment in which formula feeding is attempted. When an attempt was made to introduce formula feeding among the village people of southern Egypt, almost every baby died despite the fact that vitamin supplements were given and presumably suitable formulas prescribed.[39] Small surveys in the United States, however, tend to indicate no difference in death rate and only moderate differences in disease rate.[10, 40]

One of the best studies ever done on this controversial subject has recently been completed in Britain.[8] Every group in the population is represented in the study, which was done on a national sample of 4669 babies born in March, 1946, and followed up when two years old. The standards of artificial feeding in Britain are high. Even in 1946 the government laid great emphasis on all infants and young children getting vitamin supplements cheaply and easily, and milk powder was liberally distributed. On the other hand, the art of successful breast feeding had not been entirely lost in Britain. Fifty-three per cent of the babies were still breast fed at two months. It was, therefore, a good country to test the difference between successful breast feeding and failure to do so.

Successfully breast-fed infants whose fathers were black coated workers, manual or agricultural workers, died less frequently than their artificially fed counterparts. The death rate between the age of 8 weeks and 2 years was 18.5 per thousand for those breast fed less than 8 weeks, and 10.9 per thousand for those breast fed more than 8 weeks. Thus among those not breast fed successfully, 7 or 8 more children in each thousand died. However, this difference in mortality rates applied only to the above-mentioned classes—the mortality rate for professional and salaried classes was virtually the same for breast- and artificially-fed babies.

Gastrointestinal disturbances were also related to the type of feeding the baby received. Those breast fed less than 8 weeks were more than twice as likely to be admitted to a hospital or to die of a gastrointestinal upset.* The over-all incidence of minor gastrointestinal upsets was about the same in breast- and bottle-fed groups since some upsets characteristically occur at weaning. However, during the first four months babies who were never breast fed were most likely to have diarrhea. The average date of the first attack of diarrhea was delayed approximately six days for each month of breast feeding. This difference remained even if premature babies and babies with poor housing were excluded.

Lower respiratory infections were also less frequent among the successfully breast fed. During the first nine months breast-fed babies were less likely than bottle-fed babies to get a lower respiratory infection serious enough to be treated by a doctor or hospital. This difference was still found when sickly babies were excluded and when only the well-to-do and least crowded families were considered. Bottle-fed babies were also more likely to have repeated attacks of bronchitis and pneumonia.

* Children of salaried and professional workers were omitted in compiling this statistic since such children were likely to be treated in a nursing home rather than a hospital.

The immunity-conferring properties of breast feeding seemed to vary. Breast-fed babies contracted whooping cough, German measles, and chicken pox as frequently as the artificially fed. However, the incidence of measles among babies never breast fed was relatively high for all ages. This immunity of the breast fed persisted at least through the second year.

This relative immunity of the breast fed was found in the working class and well-to-do families, under poor living conditions and under good living conditions, and in families with or without school-age children.

How to Encourage Successful Breast Feeding

Although the evidence suggests that unsuccessful breast feeding is little more desirable than artificial feeding, successful breast feeding seems to be overwhelmingly preferable to other modes of feeding. The problem of establishing successful breast feeding is not as impossible as it sometimes seems. If institutions and physicians would stop promoting feeding methods that cause lactation failure, stop educating for artificial feeding, and stop forcing early weaning on mothers who enjoy breast feeding, there would be many more contented nursing couples.

Of course, the woman who is emotionally revolted at the idea of nursing her baby, the woman who fears the personal intimacy or personal responsibility of breast feeding, probably cannot be induced to breast feed successfully. Attempts to do so merely lead to unsuccessful breast feeding. However, there are many women who with help and encouragement are emotionally capable of breast feeding successfully—provided the interference of society can be overcome. Eliminating the following barriers will help these mothers breast feed successfully:

1. *Stop Educating for Artificial Feeding*

The slant towards artificial feeding permeates most products of our society so deeply that we are almost blind to it. For instance, recently the department of health of a great state issued an excellent booklet on reproduction which was endorsed by prominent community leaders. One whole page of this booklet was devoted to the development of hair in the girl at adolescence, but not one word of mention was made of the development of her breasts. The booklet contained fourteen anatomical drawings of the vagina and uterus, but not one of the breasts. Nor is the reproductive function of the breast once mentioned in the entire booklet. This booklet is not unique—but rather typical of the treatment breast feeding usually gets in our culture.

Most classes for mothers routinely teach *every* mother how to prepare a formula even when the mother happens to be planning to breast feed. The farewell present of many hospitals is a formula prescription or even several bottles of formula—regardless of whether the baby is breast fed or not. This is done as a kindness, yet what more powerful psychological propaganda for artificial feeding could be devised?

2. *Stop Using Feeding Methods that Cause Lactation Failure*
The most popular of these methods at present are:

A. Limiting sucking to about one fifth the amount probably needed to establish an abundant milk supply in most women. This is done by not permitting feeding until the day after delivery, by limiting the number of feedings to five or six a day, and by limiting each feeding to about three to five minutes by the clock.

B. Teaching the baby to be indifferent to the breast. This is done in two ways. First, the baby is filled up with water or formula during the first two or three days when he should be sucking a great deal to encourage milk secretion. Second, when supplemental food does become necessary, it is routinely given by bottle. A recent extensive study shows that the length of breast feeding was doubled by the simple expedient of giving supplemental food by spoon rather than by bottle.[29]

C. Encouraging the failure of the let-down reflex. This is done by limiting sucking which sets off the let-down reflex, by denying the mother peace and privacy during breast feedings, by giving her inadequate pain relief when she is in discomfort, and by giving the new mother no emotional support or encouragement about breast feeding but instead acting as if failure were expected.

3. *Stop Forcing Successfully Breast Feeding Mothers to Wean Early*
In our society there is something embarrassing about a breast feeding couple who thoroughly enjoy themselves. As the months go by the physician in charge, like almost any representative of our society, begins to feel uncomfortable. That is why, when I have talked about successful breast feeding, one of the favorite questions physicians ask is: "How do you get a successfully breast feeding mother to *stop* breast feeding?"

The answer, of course, is: "Why should you get a mother and baby to stop breast feeding provided they both enjoy it, and provided both mother and baby are getting an ample and varied diet?" Breast feeding for two or three years is entirely accepted in other parts of the world. Even in some rural parts of the United States weaning does not take place until between twelve and twenty-four months. The most helpful role for the physician is to make sure that the baby is getting a variety of other health-building foods, and that the mother is eating a diet up to the high standards recommended by the National Research Council for lactating women.

Some of the most enthusiastic mothers I know are those who have been allowed and encouraged to breast feed their babies for a year or more. They have come through the phase of frequent physiological feedings of the neonate. They and their babies have found the real companionship and personal interchange that is possible only in an older baby. Several of these mothers in a community can do more to encourage successful breast feeding in other mothers than volumes of written words and entreaties.

SUMMARY

1. A group of women who were anxious to breast feed their babies completely two or more months were compared with a group of women who expressed little desire to breast feed. Statistical analysis showed eight specific differences between these two groups.

2. These differences, in general, indicated that women who were negative toward breast feeding were also more likely to be resentful of and less efficient in certain other aspects of their female role. Women who were positive toward breast feeding were more likely to continue to breast feed successfully, to feel childbirth was easy, and to feel that women had at least as satisfying a time in life as men.

3. Other research shows that breast feeding is closely related to motherly desires and that emotions influence the secretion and expulsion of milk.

4. Successful breast feeding with its easy abundance of milk is more desirable than the usual inhibited type of breast feeding found in our society and is also more desirable than artificial feeding. Our society could produce many more contented nursing couples provided our present knowledge were actually applied in practice.

REFERENCES

1. ADAIR, F. E. Etiological factors of mammary cancer in 200 women. *New York State J. Med.* 34:61, 1934.
2. BAGG, H. J. Experimental studies concerning the functional activity of the breast in relation to mammary carcinoma in mice. *J. Cancer Res.* 9:498, 1925.

3. BAIN, KATHERINE   The incidence of breast feeding in hospitals in the United States. *Pediatrics 2:*313, 1948.

4. BLICKENSTORFER, E.   Mutterinstinkte bie einem Manne mit Krankhafter Bildung von lactotropem Hypophysenhormon. *Arch. Psychiat. 182:*536, 1949.

5. CHILDERS, A. T., and HAMIL, B. M.   Emotional problems in children as related to the duration of breast feeding in infancy. *Am. J. Orthopsychiat. 2:*134, 1932.

6. DARGENT, M., and MEYER, M.   Données étiologiques concernant la cancer du sein. *Presse méd. 56:*561, 1948.

7. DAVIS, H. V., *et al.*   Effects of cup, bottle and breast feeding on oral activities of newborn infants. *Pediatrics 2:*549, 1948.

8. DOUGLAS, J. W. B.   The extent of breast feeding in Great Britain in 1946, with special reference to the health and survival of children. *J. Obst. & Gynaec. Brit. Emp. 57:*335, 1950.

9. ELY, F., and PETERSEN, W. E.   Factors involved in the ejection of milk. *J. Dairy Sc. 24:*221, 1941.

10. FABER, H. K., and SUTTON, T. L.   A statistical comparison of breast-fed and bottle fed babies during the first year. *Am. J. Dis. Child. 40:*1163, 1930.

11. FREEMAN, MARGARET   Factors associated with length of breast feeding. *Smith College Studies in Social Work 2:*274, 1932.

12. HOEFER, CAROLYN, and HARDY, M. C.   Later development of breast fed and artificially fed infants. *J. A. M. A. 92:*615, 1929.

13. HOLWAY, A. R.   Early self-regulation of infants and later behavior in play interviews. *Am. J. Orthopsychiatry 19:*612, 1949.

14. GREENWAY, P. J.   Artificially induced lactation in humans. *East African M. J. 13:*346, 1937.

15. JEANS, P. C.   Feeding of healthy infants and children. *J. A. M. A. 142:*806, 1950.

16. LEVY, D. M.   *Maternal Overprotection.*   New York, Columbia Univ. Press, 1943.

17. MASLOW, A. H., and SZILAGYI-KESSLER, I.   Security and breast feeding. *J. Abnorm. & Social Psychol. 41:*83, 1946.

18. MEAD, MARGARET   *Sex and Temperament.*   New York, Morrow, 1935.

19. MOIR, CHASSAR   Recording the contractions of the human pregnant and non-pregnant uterus. *Trans. Edinburgh Obst. Soc. 54:*93, 1934.

20. NEWTON, M., and NEWTON, NILES   The let-down reflex in human lactation. *J. Pediat. 33:*698, 1948.

21. NEWTON, M., and NEWTON, NILES   Breast abscess: A result of lactation failure. *Surg., Gynec. & Obst. 91:*651, 1950.

22. NEWTON, M., and NEWTON, NILES   Postpartum engorgement of the breast. *Am. J. Obst. & Gynec. 61:*664, 1951.

23. NEWTON, NILES   The relationship between infant feeding experience and later behavior. *J. Pediat. 38:*28, 1951.

24. NEWTON, NILES Nipple pain and nipple damage. *J. Pediat. 41:*411, 1952.

25. NEWTON, NILES The sexual implications of breast feeding. *Child-Family Digest 7:*16, 1952.

26. NEWTON, NILES "Breast feeding." In *Transactions of the Fifth American Congress of Obstetrics and Gynecology.* St. Louis, Mo., Mosby, 1952.

27. NEWTON, NILES, and NEWTON, M. Relation of the let-down reflex to ability to breast feed. *Pediatrics 5:*726, 1950.

28. NEWTON, NILES, and NEWTON, M. Relation of ability to breast feed and maternal attitudes toward breast feeding. *Pediatrics 5:*869, 1950.

29. NEWTON, NILES, and NEWTON, M. Recent trends in breast feeding: A review. *Am. J. M. Sc. 221:*691, 1951.

30. ORLANSKY, H. Infant care and personality. *Psychol. Bull. 46:*1, 1949.

31. PETERSEN, W. E. Effects of certain hormones and drugs on the perfused mammary gland. *Proc. Soc. Exper. Biol. & Med. 50:*298, 1942.

32. PETERSEN, W. E., and LUDWICK, T. M. The humoral nature of the factor causing the let down of milk. *Federation Proc. 1:*66, 1942.

33. PETERSON, C. H., and SPANO, F. L. Breast feeding, maternal rejection and child personality. *Character and Personality 10:*62, 1941.

34. RIDDLE, O., *et al.* Maternal behavior induced in virgin rats by prolactin. *Proc. Soc. Exper. Biol. & Med. 32:*730, 1935.

35. ROBERTS, ENA Thumb and finger sucking in relation to feeding in early infancy. *Am. J. Dis. of Child. 68:*7, 1944.

36. ROGERSON, B. C. F., and ROGERSON, C. H. Feeding in infancy and subsequent psychological difficulties. *J. Ment. Sc. 85:*1163, 1939.

37. SELYE, H., and MCKOEWN, T. Effect of mechanical stimulation of nipples on ovary and sexual cycle. *Surg. Gynec. & Obst. 59:*886, 1934.

38. SPENCE, J. C. The modern decline of breast-feeding. *Brit. M. J. 2:*729, 1938.

39. STEVENSON, S. S. Comparison of breast and artificial feeding. *J. Am. Dietet. A. 25:*752, 1949.

40. STEVENSON, S. S. The adequacy of artificial feeding in infancy. *J. Pediat. 31:*616, 1947.

41. TOMPKINS, P. The histologic appearance of the endometrium during lactation amenorrhea and its relationship to ovarian function. *Am. J. Obst. & Gynec. 45:*48, 1943.

42. WALLER, H. K. A reflex governing the outflow of milk from the breast. *Lancet 1:*69, 1943.

43. WEISCHHOFF, H. A. Artificial stimulation of lactation in primitive cultures. *Bull. Hist. Med. 8:*1403, 1940.

CHAPTER 7

WOMEN'S FEELINGS ABOUT
CARE OF THEIR BABIES

FINDINGS OF OTHER RESEARCH STUDIES

There is considerable evidence that physical and social factors are related to a woman's feelings toward her babies, or conversely it may be said that a woman's feelings about her babies are related to certain physical and social phenomena.

PHYSICAL COMPONENTS IN MOTHERLY BEHAVIOR

Physical components in the desire to care for children are indicated in the research of Levy. His most extraordinary finding was quite a high relationship between *motherliness and duration of menstrual flow*. He secured this by dividing a group of mothers of problem children into high, middle, and low maternal groups. The duration of menstruation was corrected for frequency of flow. The majority of subjects who menstruated four days or less were low in maternal drive, the majority of subjects who menstruated six days were high in maternal drive, and those whose menstruation lasted five days were about equally divided between the women with middle, high, and low maternal drive.

The duration of menstrual flow was much more carefully measured in Levy's study than in this one. When he extended his research to a large number of college girls, presumably with less careful evaluations of menstruation, he too got a low negative correlation in the case of the maternal scores of Utah college girls. Smith and Brooklyn college girls,

59

on the other hand, did show a high correlation between test scores and duration of menstruation. The limitations of Levy's study and of this one should be emphasized as both depended on the woman's report of menstrual flow, and this would certainly be partly conditioned by her attitude toward it.

Physically based motherliness under some circumstances can withstand a great deal of cultural pressure in the opposite direction. Mead reports the case of a plump, soft, big-breasted Mundugumor woman, Kwenda by name, who had the misfortune of being born into a very aggressive society that prized tall, lithe, slender, unmotherly women. Kwenda loved children. She refused to throw away her first child although her husband requested it. Later when her husband refused to be reconciled with her, she had no more children but adopted a baby and breast fed it as her own.

Other evidence of the physical component in motherliness comes from its *relation to breast feeding,* as discussed in Chapter 6.

There is also considerable evidence that motherly behavior in animals is related to *hormonal changes.*[2] Animals do not care for their young out of a sense of duty. They are motivated by a physically based drive. Insofar as human beings are of animal origin, similar physical drives can be expected to exist in the human mother.

In considering the physical component in the desire to care for the baby, *dietary factors* should not be overlooked. Giving care to a baby is an active physical process, and those whose energy is diminished by faulty nutrition would naturally have less energy available for this task. This is much more than an abstract quibble. A large proportion of American mothers today suffer from improperly chosen diets. Tompkins' research indicates that vitamin deficiencies, usually subclinical, may exist in more than ninety per cent of some groups of pregnant women. Careful nutritional surveys,[5,15] indicate both middle class and poor women often have pregnancy diets far below the standards recommended by the National Research Council. Results indicate that fewer than one in four middle-class mothers have diets which contain both enough protein and enough of all the recommended vitamins and minerals.

PSYCHOLOGICAL COMPONENTS IN MOTHERLY BEHAVIOR

Unlike the physical component, the psychological and cultural components in motherliness have been very popular subjects of speculation. This speculation is based on little sound research. There has been some research on *how* a "good" mother acts toward her baby, and insight has been gained by comparative anthropological studies which contrast cultures that develop a high proportion of kind, nurturing mothers with cultures that develop a high proportion of emotionally cruel mothers. However, when it comes to the important question: "What psychological and cultural experiences differentiate the woman who likes looking after her baby and the woman who does not in the United States today?" there is but little objective evidence except what has come from dealing with the extreme cases—behavior problem children and their mothers.

Symonds' research is notable in that he did obtain a better sampling of the general population than usual. He obtained his subjects through students who contributed case histories of children of their acquaintance. He found that the mothers of accepted children more frequently had grown up in friendly, cheerful, prosperous homes with well-educated mothers and intelligent fathers, who were compatibly married. He found that mothers of rejected children had more frequently grown up in homes where educational opportunities were limited, where fear was used as a method of control by parents, and where excessive punishment or criticism was administered. These and other differences which Symonds found were slight, but they were quite consistent in their agreement with modern psychological theories. Perhaps because this study deals with the care of very young babies, social differences do not appear to be important, as they were in Symonds' study.

OTHER STUDIES OF ROOMING-IN

The study most comparable to this research was one done at Yale. Mothers were interviewed to see whether they preferred rooming-in or nursery accommodations for their babies. A highly significant relationship was found between anticipated desire to breast feed and anticipated desire to have the baby to care for. However, in the Yale study[9] well-educated white mothers with few children and who belonged to the upper occupational groups were found to be more desirous of rooming-in. Since it was just these mothers who were most apt to have read and heard about the advantages of rooming-in, the Yale findings seem reasonable. These sociological differences did not occur in this research probably because inquiries were made after the birth of the baby when rooming-in was a "fact" rather than an "idea." The differences between rooming-in as a "fact" and rooming-in presented as an "idea" has been emphasized by McBryde, whose experiences with both optional and compulsory rooming-in made him feel that the optional plan of rooming-in involved misunderstandings.

RESULTS OF THIS STUDY

Previous research gives evidence that social and physical phenomena are related to motherly emotions. This study also concentrates on women's feelings about child care and their relation to certain other aspects of women's life.

Feelings about rooming-in as they were measured in this study probably represent unusually good way of determining the mother's feelings about the care of her young baby. Each mother had in effect been put in a well-controlled experimental situation. Each mother had exactly the same equipment for looking after the baby. Each mother was relieved of all conflicting responsibilities such as household tasks and caring for the needs of other children. All were in a comparable state of health. Mothers who reacted to this real experience with joy and approval can probably be assumed to have a different attitude toward their babies from those who reacted with complaints.

Women were considered to have negative feelings about the care of their babies if they complained about rooming-in care of the baby. Some had nothing but criticism for rooming-in, while others said they liked it but then complained about having the baby brought to them too soon after birth.

Women were considered to have positive feelings about care of their babies if they had nothing but positive things to say about rooming-in. Some used strong, enthusiastic words like "love" to describe their enjoyment of it.

Women with negative feelings about care of their babies were found to differ from women with positive feelings toward the care of their babies in ten different ways.

These differences are summarized in the following paragraphs. Statistical calculations show that all of these differences are quite unlikely to have occurred by chance $(p<0.2)$. The ones that are very unlikely to have occurred by chance $(p<0.05)$ have an asterisk beside them. The statistical details can be found in Appendix D.

Feelings about rooming-in were related to *feelings about many aspects of woman's biological role*. Women who enjoyed the care of their babies were more likely to express positive feelings toward menstruation,* pregnancy, childbirth,* and breast feeding. They were apt to marry young and seldom wished to be men. Women who criticized the rooming-in system of baby care were more likely to complain about menstruation* and pregnancy. They usually thought birth was hard,* and were more often inclined to bottle feed. They even tended to put off marriage until a slightly later age, and often wished to be men.

The physical functioning of the female genital tract was also related to feelings about care of the baby in the hospital. Women who liked caring for their babies showed a considerable tendency to menstruate more copiously.* They had had fewer miscarriages, and had produced more children.* They were more frequently unsedated and fully conscious at birth. Women who complained about rooming-in care of their babies were likely to menstruate less copiously,* to have more miscarriages but fewer children,* and to receive some anesthesia and/or analgesia at delivery.

PRACTICAL IMPLICATIONS

The physical importance of the mother's desire to care for the child is so obvious that it needs little elucidation. The uncared-for infant dies; the physically neglected infant is more prone to succumb to diseases and to meet with injurious accidents. Physical care given without joy or personal interest may be psychologically crippling. Recent well-controlled objective evidence shows that human personality, and life itself, depend on *motherly* care of the baby.

Lack of Maternal Care: Its Physical Consequences

Even the most aseptic and hygienic institutional care does not provide an adequate substitute for interested individual care. Impersonal institutional care leads to a malady of hospitalism described by Bakwin as follows:

Infants under six months of age who have been in an institution for some time present a well-defined picture. The outstanding features are listlessness, emaciation and pallor, relative immobility, quietness, unresponsiveness to stimuli like a smile or a coo, indifferent appetite, failure to gain weight properly despite the ingestion of diets which, in the home, are entirely adequate, frequent stools, poor sleep, an appearance of unhappiness, proneness to febrile episodes, absence of sucking habits.

The hospitalized infant is thin and pale, but the pallor is not always associated with a reduction in hemoglobin. The facial expression is unhappy and gives an impression of misery. Muscle tone is poor and it is possible to extend the legs fully at the knees, contrasting in this way with normal young infants. There is no alteration in the deep reflexes. The infant shows no interest in his environment, lying quietly in bed, rarely crying and moving very little. Such movements as he makes are slow and deliberate, unlike the quick movements one expects at this age. Even respiration seems quieter than in normal infants.

The rapidity with which the symptoms of hospitalism begin to disappear when an afflicted baby is placed in a good home is amazing. . . . The baby promptly becomes more animated and responsive: fever, if present in the hospital, disappears in twenty-four to seventy-two hours; there is gain in weight and an improvement in color.

This malady of hospitalism predisposes to disease and death. Impersonal aseptic institutions for babies have a shockingly high mortality and morbidity rate.

Spitz[17] describes a foundling home where the most hygienic precautions were taken and where every child showed symptoms of hospitalism. Medical rounds were made daily and each young child lived in an isolated cubicle. The institution was swept with an epidemic of measles— every child contracting the disease. In spite of liberal administration of convalescent serum and globulins, more than 25 per cent (23 out of 88) of the children under 2½ years died. Outside of the foundling home, in the same community the mortality rate from measles during the first year of life was less than 0.5 per cent. Although normally the highest mortality rate for children infected with measles is found among babies, in the foundling home it was the children between 1½ and 2½ years who had the highest mortality rate—a mortality rate of close to 40 per cent. Presumably these children had suffered from lack of motherly care for more months than in the case of the younger children.

In 1930 Bellevue Hospital started a campaign to give babies special motherlike attention rather than just the usual impersonal routine care. Their death rate for children under one year fell steadily from 30 to 35 per cent to less than 10 per cent in eight years. Most of the fall in mortality took place before the advent of modern chemotherapy.[1]

A survey done in 1915[6] indicated that commitment to institutional care was virtually a death sentence to babies. The mortality rate was about 400 to 600 per thousand per year, or even higher, in various institutions over the country. Chapin studied ten infant asylums in different United States cities. The deaths per year constituted 32 to 75 per cent of their admissions per year. A New York State Department of Charities report found in a survey of eleven institutions that their average death rate was 422 per 1000 babies—five times as high as the mortality rate of babies of the same age in New York State as a whole.

Knox followed up 200 infants admitted to various institutions in the city of Baltimore. Of these between 89 and 90 per cent died within a year. The 10 per cent that lived apparently did so because they were taken from the institutions for short times and given into the care of foster mothers or relatives. The associated Charities Clinic in San Francisco had a mortality of 56 per cent the year before boarding out was begun.[11] With the initiation of foster homes with medical care the mortality dropped to 3 per cent—a very low figure for that era.

Bakwin's study of the problem leads him to feel that although babies are not dying in large numbers in institutions in the United States today, the problem of the inadequacy of impersonal institutional care has not been solved. It has been by-passed with foster home and foster mothers, and individual motherly care whenever possible.

LACK OF MATERNAL CARE: ITS PSYCHOLOGICAL CONSEQUENCES

Recently there has been a growing recognition of the fact that maternal care—or lack of it—is equally important psychologically. Psychological theorists, particularly Suttie and Bevan-Brown, emphasize that the mother-child relationships are the most fundamental of all personality-shaping forces. There are a considerable number of objective facts that seem to be in line with these theories. Children receiving unmotherly institutional care are emotionally and intellectually handicapped as well as physically weakened.

When Gesell and Amatruda studied institutionalized babies, they found that by eight to twelve weeks of life they were acting differently from the average baby brought up at home. They showed diminished interest and reactivity. By the time they were half a year old they showed general retardation, lacked the usual initiative, and had a notably bland facial expression. By about a year they began to differ from mothered babies in that they were inept in new social situations, showed exaggerated resistance to new situations, and showed retarded language behavior.

Spitz studied the development of four groups of babies. The first group was born into professional families and remained at home. The second group was born in a very poor, isolated fishing village and remained at home. The third group was born to delinquent girls in a penal institution and was cared for by its mothers. The fourth group was of assorted heredity and taken care of in a foundling home where there was excellent hygienic care but virtually no mothering. All three groups who were allowed to remain in their mothers' care developed normally. The average development quotient of these "mothered" groups was virtually the same at the beginning and end of their first year of life. Those deprived of mothering started with a development quotient almost as high as that of the babies born to professional families. By the end of the first year, their development quotient had fallen precipitously. It was well below the lowest of the other groups, and only three-fifths as high as it was at the beginning of the year.

Another study demonstrating that individual motherly attention is the important factor in the baby's development was done by Rheingold on babies in foster homes. She compared the babies who were cared for along with other young babies by a foster mother with those who were the foster mothers' only baby. The development as tested by the Gesell Development Schedule showed that those who got undivided attention were accelerated while those who had to share attention with other babies were retarded to a statistically significant[4] extent. Twice as many "only" babies were socially responsive and outgoing.

The psychological importance of the mother to the baby is further shown by what happens to the baby when it loses its mother. The baby may go into a profound emotional disturbance even when a substitute mother is provided and even when other factors in the environment stay the same.

Spitz[18] studied 123 such children who were looked after in an institution by their own mothers until the age of about seven months. Then they were given over to the care of another woman. Thirty-seven per cent of these babies reacted with such severe symptoms that, had they been older, they would have been considered psychiatric cases. They showed apprehension, weepiness, dejection, and even stupor. They began to ignore people and became uninterested in their surroundings. Many lost appetite, refused to eat, and lost weight. Some had difficulty sleeping. Given mental tests their development quotients fell on the average of twenty-three points immediately after the separation from their mothers. Thereafter their development quotients continued to fall, but at a slower rate. The first test after restoration to the mother showed a twenty-four point rise, and other symptoms rapidly disappeared.

Repeated studies done in several countries have found that young children, as well as babies, are retarded by lack of motherly care. The study of Goldfarb is typical of these findings. He studied 30 three-year-olds, half of whom had been in institutions and half of whom had been in foster homes from the time they were about four and a half months old. The foster home children had considerably higher I.Q.'s. Two different intelligence tests showed statistically significant differences. One could expect the influence of heredity to be in an opposite direction, since the mothers of the institutional children had the superior occupational status.

There is considerable evidence that failure to have maternal care in the early years leaves a mark for life. For example, Thies studied two contrasting groups who were of similar heredity. As children, both groups had been placed in foster homes of about the same quality and at similar ages. The one difference was that one group of children had spent five years or more of their childhood in institutions, and the others had spent those years at home. In spite of the fact that 80 per cent of the homes were considered bad homes, the children who had lived at home were better adjusted to a statistically significant extent. Only 65.5 per cent of the institution group were socially capable adults as compared with 82 per cent of the noninstitutionalized children. Twice as many of the institutional children turned out to be on trial, in institutions, or gave other indications of behavior harmful to society.

Bowlby, who has done an extraordinary work in summarizing the research on the influence of maternal care on mental health for the World Health Organization, cites studies done in many countries—and almost all tending in more or less the same direction. Again and again, in country after country, the same broad tendency emerges—that infants and young children deprived of motherly care tend to be seriously handicapped psychologically. He eloquently writes: ". . . the evidence is now such that it leaves no room for doubt regarding the general proposition—that the prolonged deprivation of the young child of maternal care may have grave and far-reaching effects on his character and so on the whole of his future life. . . . Reluctance to accept it is, perhaps, because to do so would involve far-reaching changes in conceptions of human nature and in methods of caring for young children."

WHAT OF THE FUTURE?

I recently witnessed a typical scene of our civilization enacted on the maternity floor of a large hospital. The mother of a newborn baby lay elaborately dolled-up in bed. Every few hours during the day the baby was brought in to her and taken away again in a few minutes. The baby had a particularly piercing cry, and screamed before it came in to its mother and after it left its mother, and often from the nursery its particular screech could be heard. What did the mother do about it? The hospital had rooming-in arrangement upon request, and she could have had the baby to comfort had she deeply desired it. Instead, she occupied herself by hiring a television set and had it going from early morning till late at night.

It is a disturbing fact that in many hospitals where mothers can have their babies to care for, they do *not* choose to do so. Part of this hesitancy is undoubtedly due to misunderstanding of the plan. For instance, in the Jefferson Hospital wards where rooming-in was compulsory, the great majority said they enjoyed it. Part of the hesitancy is due to the fact that some obstetricians encourage their patients *not* to have rooming-in, and hospital visiting rules discriminate against rooming-in mothers. Then, too, the fashion for the operative type of obstetrics with its heavy sedation and instrumental manipulation may leave the mother unusually weak. Nevertheless, the refusal to demand rooming-in indicates that many mothers do not yearn to look after their babies, but may prefer to postpone the day.

Nor do these negative feelings necessarily disappear. Who has not heard young matrons talking about having their conventional two children early in their marriage and close together in order to "get it over with"? They expect the child-bearing years—the years when they care for babies and young children—to be disagreeable years!

METHODS OF HELPING WOMEN ENJOY MOTHERHOOD

Perhaps one of the most important questions before our society today is: How can we help women *enjoy* being mothers and thus provide good maternal care for future generations? In order to know how to help them we must know the *causes* of their lack of enjoyment.

The results of this study indicate that the answer must be looked for in several different fields—psychology, physiology, sociology, and particularly psychosomatics. Until more research is available, the following measures might help more women to enjoy motherhood:

1. *Enlightened medical management* of the mother which helps her accept her natural biological functions. The results of this study emphasize the possible importance of trying to build up more positive attitudes. It was women who accepted menstruation, pregnancy, childbirth, and breast feeding who more frequently enjoyed the care of the baby.

Unfortunately at present it seems easier to help a woman express negative feelings than to re-educate her. It seems easier to suppress lactation than to teach the mother how to breast feed successfully. It seems easier to separate the mother and the baby at birth in the hospital than to teach her how to care for the baby. It seems easier to drug the woman into unconsciousness rather than to teach her the techniques that make birth a more welcome experience.

The fact that now a childbearing woman must go to a hospital—a place no one else goes to unless they are sick—is a forceful reminder that all births tend to be considered abnormal in our society. A "Mother's Home" where prenatal guidance, obstetrical care, and pediatric guidance are all given together would do much to change habits of thinking about women's biological functions.

The liberal use of doctors' helpers would also be of help. The typical physician today is a man of superior intelligence and education who has had many years of training in the treatment of disease. His help in the treatment of disease is indispensable; but is he the right person to give routine care to healthy, childbearing women and their healthy babies? Such routine care is likely to be boring and uninteresting to him, and these feelings may influence his care of the patient.

Much of the work that American pediatricians and obstetricians do is carried on by well-trained women of superior character in some other countries. They have been thoroughly trained in the task of guiding *healthy* mothers and babies. They are trained to spot abnormality and refer it. They save the physician untold work and at the same time it is easier for them to do the work because that is their chief interest. For instance, sitting with a woman throughout a long, normal labor can be emotionally satisfying to such women; whereas it may frankly be a nuisance to a man who has been trained for more intricate and complicated things.

2. *Instruction and research designed to stimulate thinking about positive aspects of motherhood.* There is a tendency in our society either to ignore or to depreciate motherhood to an extreme degree. For instance, recently a book came out which was hailed by the critics as one of the great comprehensive books about women. Out of more than 700 pages, only 43 were devoted to women as mothers—and a considerable portion of these 43 pages was spent in discussing abortion. The rest for the most part emphasized the feelings of dislike that some women have toward their children.

Of course there are women who dislike being mothers and dislike their children; but there are also women who like being mothers and like their children. Nevertheless, few modern novels or even modern scientific papers deal with the woman who likes her children or whose children like her! Instead it is fashionable to discuss women who hate or cripple their children emotionally, or who use their children to satisfy their own immature emotions. It is even fashionable to take the point of view that the so-called satisfactions of motherhood are merely the satisfactions gained from domination of a weaker person!

This depreciation of motherhood may be one of the causes of women's envy of men. If a woman receives ample recognition for her unique biological gifts, she might be less envious of the privileges and prerogatives that society bestows on men. The importance of this point is suggested by a finding of this study. The women who envied men to the extent of wishing to be men were slightly more apt to dislike the care of their babies.

3. *Counseling help for mothers.* There is a real need for skilled mothers' advisers who concentrate on helping mothers in their problems with

their children. At present informal advice is given by teachers or physicians or other persons who may not have much experience with the everyday practical problems of motherhood. Then, too, they do not usually have the time to allow the mother to talk out her problem in full. Nor do the counseling professions offer just the kind of help needed, at present. Marriage counseling centers on the husband-wife relationship and parents-child relationships are usually viewed as secondary by-products. Clinics for problem children usually deal only with mothers whose children have severe problems. Mothers' counseling requires specialized knowledge (about homemaking, child care, etc.) as well as the general counseling skills.

The moderately well-adjusted women with the moderately well-adjusted children still have problems like:

"Sometimes I get so mad at that child I am afraid I'll hurt him. Isn't there something very wrong about this? It worries me."

"My youngest is two and my other children are in school. The boss I worked for before I was married wants me back. We need the money. Will I hurt the children if I go back to work?"

"I have a cute baby—everybody says so. But I just can't feel warm inside about him the way some mothers seem to. How can I get to liking him more?"

"The children never do anything unless I remind and scold them all the time. My husband says I nag at them too much—but how else can I get them to do what is right?"

Instead of struggling alone with these problems, it would be helpful to talk them over with a mother's counselor, who would be easily available at a "Mother's Home" (mentioned in Point 1). This would be the first step to a psychiatrist for some mothers. Most, however, might find that just a chance to talk over their problems would help them feel better, and/or help them find a workable plan for easing their worries.

SUMMARY

1. The group of women who complained about having to look after their babies in the hospital were compared with the group of women who enjoyed looking after their babies. Statistical analysis showed ten specific differences between these two groups.

2. These differences, in general, indicated that women who disliked looking after their babies were also more likely to have negative feelings about other aspects of their biological role and to be physically less effi-

cient and less productive females. Women who liked caring for their babies were more apt to have positive feelings about menstruation and childbirth and other aspects of their biological role. They were also more likely to have copious menstrual flows, more children, and to present no obstetrical problems.

3. Other research also indicates that motherly behavior is related to menstrual flow, breast feeding, hormonal changes, and some other physical and social factors.

4. The lack of loving motherly care can have serious psychological and physical consequences. More research is greatly needed to answer one of the most important questions before our society today: How can we help women *enjoy* being mothers, and thus provide good maternal care for future generations?

REFERENCES

1. BAKWIN, H. Emotional deprivation in infants. *J. Pediat. 35:*512, 1949.
2. BEACH, F. A. *Hormones and Behavior.* New York, Hoeber, 1948.
3. BEVAN-BROWN, M. *The Sources of Love and Fear.* New York, Vanguard, 1950.
4. BOWLBY, J. *Maternal Care and Mental Health.* Geneva, World Health Organization, 1952, p. 46.
5. BURKE, B. S. *et al.* The influence of nutrition during pregnancy upon the condition of the infant at birth. *J. Nutrition 26:*569, 1943.
6. CHAPIN, H. D. A plea for accurate statistics in infants' institutions. *Trans. Am. Pediat. Coll. 27:*180, 1915.
7. GESELL, A., and AMATRUDA, C. S. *Development Diagnosis: Normal and Abnormal Child Development: Clinical Methods and Pediatric Application.* New York, Hoeber, 1941.
8. GOLDFARB, W. Effects of psychological deprivation in infancy and subsequent stimulation. *Am. J. Psychiat. 102:*18, 1945.
9. KLATSKIN, E. H., *et al.* Choice of rooming-in or newborn nursery. *Pediatrics 6:*878, 1950.
10. KNOX, Discussion of paper by Chapin.[6]
11. LEVY, D. M. Psychosomatic studies of some aspects of maternal behavior. *Psychosom. Med. 4:*223, 1942.
12. MCBRYDE, A. Compulsory rooming-in in the ward and private newborn service at Duke. *J. A. M. A. 145:*625, 1951.
13. MEAD, M. *From the South Seas.* New York, Morrow, 1939.
14. MONTGOMERY, T. L., *et al.* Observation on the rooming-in program of baby with mother in ward and private service. *Am. J. Obst. & Gynec. 57:*176, 1949.

15. MOORE, M. C., *et al.* Food habits of women during pregnancy. *J. Am. Dietet. A. 23:*847, 1947.
16. RHEINGOLD, H. L. Mental and social development of infants in relation to the number of other infants in the boarding home. *Am. J. Orthopsychiat. 13:*41, 1943.
17. SPITZ, R. A. Hospitalism: An inquiry into the genesis of psychiatric conditions in early childhood. *The Psychoanalytic Study of the Child, I,* 1945.
18. SPITZ, R. A. Anaclitic depression. *The Psychoanalytic Study of the Child, II,* 1946.
19. SUTTIE, I. D. *The Origins of Love and Hate.* New York, Julian Press, 1952.
20. SYMONDS, P. M. *The Psychology of Parent-Child Relationships.* New York, Appleton, 1939.
21. THIES, S. VAN S. *How Foster Children Turn Out.* New York, State Charities Aid Association, Publication No. 165, as quoted by Bowlby.[4]
22. TOMPKINS, W. T. The clinical significance of nutritional deficiencies in pregnancy. *Bull. New York Acad. Med. 24:*375, 1948.

CHAPTER 8

WOMEN'S ENVY OF MEN

FINDINGS OF OTHER RESEARCH STUDIES

Research evidence indicates that women who wish to be men and women who feel men have an easier time in life have different feelings about some other areas of their lives as well.

DESIRE TO BE A MAN: RELATION TO OTHER FEELINGS

There can be little doubt that the wish to be a man is related to other important feelings in American women. The *Fortune* Survey compared feelings of the women who would like to be men with the feelings of all the women polled. Their results[2] were as follows:

	Percentage of women who would like to be men who feel that:	*Percentage of all women polled who feel that:*
Men have an easier time	59	41
Men have a more interesting time	49	36
Wife should decide how family money is spent	29	23
Men are more extravagant in spending money	36	30
All women should have an equal chance with men for any job	33	28

73

These differences suggest that women who wish to be men tend to have more faith in women's abilities, but also tend to envy men more than the average women.

The results of the *Fortune* Survey must be taken as scientific facts of first-rate importance.[1] The *Fortune* Surveys use the most modern methods of objective psychology and apply them on a national scale. The questions are carefully worded so as not to be loaded, and are pretested before they are included in the national survey. The interviews are conducted by competent interviewers, who are carefully supervised. No list of persons is used but the sample is so picked as to represent the United States population in regard to age, sex, income level, race, geography, and size of location. Between 3500 and 5000 people are interviewed in each survey and, generally speaking, the probable error usually is a very low one—in the neighborhood of 2 per cent.

FEELING THAT MEN'S LIFE IS "EASIEST": RELATION TO OTHER FEELINGS

The *Fortune* Surveys also asked another question which probably measured the envy of men to some extent. They asked: "On the whole, and considering people in all walks of life, who do you think has the easier time in present day America, men or women?" Their results were as follows:

	Percentage of women who think men have an easier time who feel that:	Percentage of all women polled who feel that:
A wife should decide about how the family money is spent	30	23
Men have less ability to make decisions	28	23
Men have a more interesting time	45	36

These differences suggest that when compared with the average woman, women who think *men* have an easier time in life more often believe that *women* are more capable of making decisions. Their envy of men is shown further in their more frequent belief that men have the most interesting time in life.

The *Fortune* Survey suggests that as the economic status rises among women, the feeling that *women* have the easiest time in life increases. Twenty-five per cent of the lowest income bracket said they thought women had an easier time in life, as compared with 39 per cent of the upper middle income group and 47 per cent of the women of the highest economic level.

RESULTS OF THIS STUDY

Two measures were used in attempts to ascertain women's envy of men in this study. The direct question "Have you ever wished you were a man?" was used and also the more indirect one "Do you think men or do you think women have a more satisfying time in life?" These questions measured somewhat different feelings in the women. However, both measures were considered to show envy of men.

Women were considered to have no wish to be men if they denied ever wishing to be a man. Women were considered to wish to be men if they said they had wished to be men. This included those women who made unqualified statements as well as those who said only that they wished to be a man sometimes, when they were younger or during childbirth.

Women were considered to feel satisfaction in leading a woman's life if they avoided showing envy for men's life. Some of these women said they felt women had a better or more satisfying time in life, while others said satisfaction in life depended on circumstance rather than sex. Still others said men and women have about the same amount of satisfaction. Women were considered to feel that men had a more satisfying time in life if they showed envy or jealousy of men's life. Such women sometimes said they felt men had a more satisfying or better time in life than women. At other times they merely said woman's life was worse.

Women who wished to be men were compared with women who did not wish to be men. They differed from each other in fourteen different ways.

Women who felt men had the most satisfying time in life were compared with the women who showed no such feelings. They differed from each other in eight different ways.

These differences are summarized in the following paragraphs. Statistical calculations show that all of these differences are quite unlikely to have occurred by chance ($p < 0.2$); the ones that are very unlikely to have occurred by chance ($p < 0.05$) have an asterisk beside them. The statistical details can be found in Appendix D.

Both groups that showed envy of men were alike in their *respect for masculinity*. Women who wished to be men were more likely to feel men had a more satisfying time in life and to want boy babies. Women who felt men had a more satisfying time in life were more likely to wish to be men, and to want boy babies. Women who did not envy men were more apt to want girl babies.

Both groups that showed envy of men *disliked some aspects of women's biological role*. Women who felt men had a more satisfying time in life were more likely to prefer artificial feedings* and to be sedated or anesthetized for childbirth. Women who actually wished to be men were more apt to complain about pregnancy* and also slightly more likely to complain about menstruation and care of the baby.

In spite of this dislike of some aspects of women's biological role, women who expressed envy of men were *unusually adequate in their exercise of their female bodies in some ways*. Both groups tended to have slightly more children than those who did not show envy of men. Women who felt men had a more satisfying time in life emphasized the *menstruation-intercourse* portion of their female functions; while those who wished to be men emphasized the *lactation portion* of the female cycle.

Although women who wished to be men did not say they wanted to breast feed, they actually were successful at breast feeding. They were likely to breast feed more successfully both in the hospital and six weeks thereafter than women who did not wish to be men. On the other hand, they were apt to report slightly less menstrual flow than women who did not wish to be men. They were also less likely to be involved in the production of illegitimate children.*

In contrast to this, women who felt men had a more satisfying time in life more frequently reported a copious menstrual flow,* and less pain at menstruation.* They were likely to desire sexual intercourse more frequently than the others but did not seem to enjoy it more than the others.

Unlike the feelings discussed in previous chapters, the envy of men is based not so much on specific physical experience, but on more generalized experiences of many sorts. Therefore it is not surprising to find that *social factors are important*. Women born before 1920 were slightly more likely to feel men had a more satisfying time in life and were definitely more likely to wish to be men.* Women who wished to be men also tended to be Catholics rather than Protestant, and to belong to the unskilled or semiskilled occupational groups. Women who wished to be men were more likely to work after marriage than women who did not wish to be men.*

PRACTICAL APPLICATIONS

EXTENT OF WOMEN'S ENVY OF MEN

According to answers given in the *Fortune* poll, 91 per cent of American men would like to be men if they were born over again. Only 66 per cent of American women said they wanted to be born as women again. More women wanted to be born men, more did not answer the question, and more "didn't know." The first fact that stands out about these statistics is that the majority of women as well as the majority of men are content enough with their sexually determined roles to say they would wish to undertake them again.

However, there is a sizable minority of women who are so discontented with their sex that they may definitely wish to be men. Twenty-five per cent frankly stated they wished to be reborn men, whereas only 3 per cent of the men said they would like to be reborn women. Probably an even larger percentage of women have some real and deep feelings of discontent—but not enough to go to the ultimate extreme of wishing to give up all womanhood.

WHY DO WOMEN ENVY MEN?

What are the factors that may contribute to this discontent? Fortunately, there is a sizable body of objective facts of national scope that can be used to help find the answer to this question. The facts seem to indicate that American women have equality in the home, but experience a great and pervasive discrimination against them outside of the home.

FAMILY LIFE A SOURCE OF ENVY

The findings of the *Fortune* Survey suggest that by and large women seem to have an equal say in the home—even to the point of deciding how the family money should be spent. Only 27 per cent of the American men questioned in the *Fortune* Survey felt that men should have the most to say about where the money went. Forty-six per cent felt the wife should have an equal say, and 16 per cent felt the wife should have more say than their husbands!

In the area of parenthood, there was a strong tendency among men to feel that women should have an equal or even greater amount of responsibility than men. Only 12 per cent of the men felt that men should have the most to say about when to have children, whereas 37 per cent felt that women should have the most to say in the matter, and 36 per cent felt it should be an equally shared decision. Only 7 per cent of the men felt they should have the most to say about disciplining the children, whereas 37 per cent wanted to have less responsibility than women. Forty-nine per cent—almost half of the men—felt that children's discipline was a matter to be shared equally by husband and wife.

In contrast to the strong feeling of women's rights and duties in regard to children, there is a tendency to feel that men should decide where the family is going to locate—presumably because of the importance of the job. Forty-eight per cent of the men felt that men should have the most say about family location—whereas only 35 per cent felt the wife should have equal say. However, for decisions that do not involve the job, there was a very strong tendency to feel that husband and wife should have equal rights. For instance, in deciding where to go on vacation, 64 per cent of the men felt that husband and wife should have equal say, whereas only 12 per cent felt that men should have superior rights.

Men and women were considered equally responsible for preserving the institution of marriage. Sixty-four per cent of the men felt that both partners were equally to blame most often when marriage was not a success, and only 11 per cent felt women were more often to blame than men. In spite of all the talk about the double standard, 67 per cent of the men felt it was just as wrong for a husband to be unfaithful to his wife as it was for a wife to be unfaithful to her husband. Only 22 per cent stated that it was worse for the wife to be unfaithful.

It should be noted that although the majority of men concede women equality and responsibility within the home and family, a minority definitely did not do so. Women who have such men as fathers or husbands would have some reason to feel that they are considered an inferior sort of human being. Likely outcomes of being exposed to such men might be deep feelings of inferiority and envy.

There were, indeed, a minority of women in the *Fortune* Survey who seemed imbued with this sense of inferiority. They declared that *men* should have more say than women as to how the family money is spent (11 per cent), where to go on family vacations (13 per cent), and even when to have children (7 per cent)! Such women as mothers may be a potent force in making their daughters feel inferior or envious of men's prerogatives.

THE WORLD OUTSIDE THE HOME AS A SOURCE OF ENVY

Whereas only a minority of men and women hold discriminating attitudes against women within the family circle, the majority of them hold discriminating attitudes towards women in the world outside the home, and in the economic world.

Employers tend to distrust women for positions of responsibility. *Fortune* Survey polled the feelings of professional men and executives (i.e., potential employers). They found that 66 per cent of them believed women have less ability to make decisions than men. Only 7 per cent believed women have more ability to make decisions than men. This may be one reason for the fact that proportionately many more men than women are employed as managers, officials, and proprietors.[4] Excluding farm owners and tenants, 9 per cent of all men employed, and only 3 per cent of all women employed, fall in this class—a ratio of three to one.[4]

Women working in the same types of occupation as men have roughly about half as much income as men. The figures are as follows:

	Median total money income of employed civilians over 14 years of age in April, 1951[4]	
	Men	*Women*
Professional, technical, and kindred workers	$4,073	$2,175
Managers, officials, and proprietors, except farm	3,814	1,674
Clerical and kindred workers	3,103	2,074
Sales workers	3,137	1,109
Operatives and kindred workers	2,790	1,661
Service workers, except private household	2,303	913

Women get roughly half as much pay as men who have had equal educations. The figures are as follows:

	Median civilian money earnings in 1946 for urban and rural non-farm earners 25 years old and over[4]	
	Men	*Women*
7 or 8 years of grade school	$2,241	$ 954
4 years high school	2,513	1,370
college—1 year or more	3,178	1,655

Although everybody is aware of the problem of discrimination against Negroes, few realize that white women get less pay than Negro men. The median wage or salary income of non-white men employed for money in 1950 over the age of 13 was $1,828. The corresponding figure for white women was $1,698.

Women's colleges were founded to give women opportunities outside the home, yet 86 per cent of Protestant women's college presidents and 72 per cent of their trustees are men.[3] The degree of discrimination can be better realized if put in reverse terms. What if Harvard, Yale, and most other male colleges had women for college presidents and had a board of trustees composed chiefly of women?

In our modern society income is an important factor in life. Income to some extent determines social class. Successes, achievement, and personal worth are also measured by the money yardstick to some extent. More than half of American women over 14 have no income whatsoever.[4] They are entirely dependent on other people for every cent they spend, and all the social values that come with money. Such dependence on the *source* of money cannot help but have psychological repercussions even though the *management* of the money is shared. In contrast to women's dependent state, 90 per cent of American men of 14 or over have an income.[4]

ENVY OF MEN'S SEXUAL ROLE

In spite of these discriminations, there are those who believe that woman's wish to be a man is not based so much on her social and family experience but on her innate envy of men's sexual role.

There is, of course, evidence that some women do envy men's sexual equipment—just as there is evidence that men envy women's ability to have babies. One has but to watch little girls trying to imitate their fathers going to the bathroom, and to see little boys tenderly mothering dolls and even trying to breast feed them in imitation of their mothers, to realize that there is some desire to act like the opposite sex. These feelings may well be important factors in developing the personality structure in some people.

However, facts indicate that this may be only a minor cause of women's prevalent wish to be men. In the *Fortune* Survey, less than 3 per cent of both men and women mentioned childbearing as a factor in believing that men had an easier time in life. The most popular reasons given for believing men had an easier time were shorter work hours and fewer family responsibilities, i.e., social rather than biological differences.

The results of this study indicate that the wish to be a man is very sensitive to social conditions. Far more than any other measure studied in this research, it varied with social influences. Women who worked after marriage, women born before 1920, Catholic women, and women belonging to the unskilled and semiskilled occupational groups all showed more tendency to wish to be men than women not in these groups.

How Discrimination Against Women May Hurt Men and Children

Although it is women who suffer inequalities in recognition, opportunity, and responsibility, the effects of this discrimination may be unhappiness for men and children as well as for the women themselves. For instance, this study found that the women who showed envy for men were more likely to wish for boy babies—presumably to compensate for their own feelings of inferiority. It is quite likely that this wish for a boy baby may carry over into a special attachment to the son. Such an attachment might bring grief to both mother and son, because it would be based, in part, on negative feelings of inadequacy and envy. This study also found that the women who wished to be men were more likely to complain about menstruation and pregnancy. Husbands of such women would feel the repercussions.

The women in this study who wished to be men showed very mixed and ambivalent feelings which would tend to cause emotional conflicts within the family. They tended to desire more intercourse than other women, but did not seem to enjoy it more than other women. They tended to have more children than women who did not wish to be men, but showed a slight tendency to dislike the care of their babies. They breast fed their babies although they expressed no particular preference for breast feeding—and thus might have the tendency to wean their babies suddenly in order to resolve the differences between attitude and behavior.

Women who showed their envy of men by feeling men had a more satisfying time in life also showed definite conflicts that would influence the lives of their family. They tended to have more children and to menstruate more copiously, yet tended to dislike the idea of breast feeding and to need escape from the experience of childbirth with drugs.

There is a tremendous need for further research in this area, because the few pieces of information that are available at present suggest that discrimination against women may affect the happiness of men, women, and children—and thus every member of the community.

Two Ways of Meeting the Problem of Discrimination

Meanwhile there are two ways of trying to meet the problem of discrimination against women. One is to pretend that women are exactly the same as men. The other is to place equal values on women's contributions to society.

Women are not the same as men. They menstruate. They get pregnant. They have babies. They breast feed. Thus they have a unique physically based tie with the infant and young child. All of these factors are related to their emotions, feelings, and even to their health—as the previous chapters of this book have shown. Utopian dreams of a society where women are treated just like men ignore the biological role of women, particularly in their childbearing years. The fact that such theories are popular is an excellent example of the extent to which our society ignores and depreciates motherhood as an important aspect of life.

There are, however, other constructive trends in modern society that may—if they continue—do much to alleviate women's envy of men while still recognizing the importance of women's unique biologically determined role.

More income going directly to women in recognition of their work contribution to society will tend to make them feel less envious of men. Mothers of children need special help. The economic contributions of mothers of young children might be recognized by special large income tax concession to families with young children, and by family allowances paid to mothers as is already done in Canada and elsewhere. Part-time jobs can help, especially as the children get older. Much of the accounting and secretarial work which is now done in offices could be done by women working at home, while the children nap or play. Someday some businesses may find that it is just as efficient to transport the work to the person as to transport the person to the work thus incurring the heavy expense of housing them during working hours. Such a change would greatly benefit homemakers.

When most women have some income the pressure to keep men's income higher than women's will ease. Results of the *Fortune* Survey show that the majority of the population believes in the theory that equal work deserves equal pay. The hesitancy to do so may be partly due to the fear that fathers will not be able to support their families if women are given economic equality. The tragedy of this discrimination is that widows and single women with families to support suffer great financial hardship, while other women may merely suffer from feelings of inadequacy or resentment.

Perhaps even more important than income is the growing appreciation of parenthood. The desire for parenthood seems to be on the increase, after decades of decline. The birth rate is considerably higher now than it was in the two decades before 1945.[4] This increased desire for children automatically puts more importance on women's unique biological role. Natural, cooperative childbirth, breast feeding, and tender, loving care of babies are again becoming fashionable. The same trend helps fathers to take more interest in their children and to spend more time with them. As a father takes on more responsibility for the care of his children, a mother's full-time burden may turn into a shared joy. These changes in attitudes may do much to help women enjoy being women.

SUMMARY

1. The group of women who said they wished to be men were compared with the group of women who said they did not wish to be men. Statistical analysis showed fourteen specific differences between these two groups.

2. The group of women who said they felt men had a more satisfying time in life were compared with women who felt men did *not* necessarily have a more satisfying time in life. Statistical analysis showed eight specific differences between these two groups.

3. Women who said they wished to be men and women who said they felt men had a more satisfying time in life were considered to show envy of men. Both groups of women who showed envy of men also showed respect for masculinity in other ways, and disliked some other aspects of their female reproductive role. However, both groups who showed envy of men were unusually adequate in the exercise of their female bodies in some ways. Women who felt men had a more satisfying time in life were more likely to emphasize the menstruation-intercourse portions of their female functions; while those who wished to be men were more likely to emphasize the lactation portion of the female cycle. Envy of men varied with several environmental factors. Women born before 1920 and women who worked after marriage were particularly likely to wish to be men.

4. Additional information comes from a *Fortune* Survey. This survey found that women who said they wished to be reborn men and who said they felt men had an easier time in life were more likely to express some other negative attitudes toward men, and to have faith in women's abilities.

5. Women's envy of men is likely to hurt their husbands and their children as well as themselves. More recognition of the values of motherhood and fair income for women's work would do much to mitigate

women's envy of men. At present most women experience severe discrimination against them outside the home, and a minority also experience discrimination within the family circle.

REFERENCES

1. Fortune   *The Fortune Survey and How it is Conducted.*   New York, Time, 1946.
2. "Fortune Survey"   *Fortune 34:5* (Aug.), 1946; and *34:5* (Sept.), 1946.
3. Nimkoff, M. F., and Wood, A.   Women's place academically. *J. Higher Education 20:28,* 1949.
4. United States Bureau of Census   *Statistical Abstracts of the United States 1952* (ed. 73). Washington, D. C., Government Printing Office 1952.

CHAPTER 9

SEXUAL INTERCOURSE: ITS RELATION TO THE REST OF WOMEN'S SEXUAL ROLE

Sexual intercourse is, of course, just as important a phase of women's reproductive role as menstruation, pregnancy, childbirth, and lactation. However, it has often been singled out as if it were the *only* important part of women's sexuality and unrelated to any other phase of women's sexual role. An excellent example of this cultural tendency is to be seen in Kinsey, *et al.*'s book on women. A huge volume purporting to cover *Sexual Behavior of the Human Female* deals in fact only with the orgastic and coital aspects of female sexuality. Menstruation, pregnancy, childbirth, and breast feeding are simply excluded from serious consideration as if they were not part of women's sexual behavior. The Kinsey study concentrates on only those portions of women's sexual behavior that are similar to what men experience. The fact that this discrepancy was seldom, if at all, noticed by reviewers shows that Kinsey *et al.*'s habits of thought are in keeping with those of most of the culture.

Actually, there is considerable research evidence that feeling about intercourse may be closely related to every other phase of women's sexuality. The evidence is as follows:

MENSTRUATION AND INTERCOURSE

Sexual feeling and sexual activity vary with the menstrual cycle. McCance, Luff, and Widdowson studied the cyclic behavior through detailed and extensive daily records made by 167 normal women—each over a period of several months. They analyzed 780 complete menstrual cycles. Inaccuracies due to memory were kept to a minimum since records were made daily through each cycle. They found that single women reached a peak of sexual feeling at about the eighth day after the onset of menstruation, with the period of lowest incidence of sexual feeling during the early part of the menstrual flow. Married women similarly experienced a low of sexual feeling during the first days of the menstrual flow, and then their incidence of desire rose rapidly to reach its peak on the eighth day. Intercourse in married women also reached its peak incidence on the eighth day and its low point during the first three days after the onset of menstruation.

Questionnaire methods have also found that women report variations in desire, according to the phase of the menstrual cycle, but they suggested a later peak for the period of greatest sexual desire.[5] This latter finding, however, might well be discounted since more accurate methods indicate earlier peaks of desire, and since these early peaks are more in accord with new research suggesting that ovulation usually takes place well before the middle of the menstrual cycle.[2]

Additional evidence about the relation of menstruation and intercourse comes from a study of menstrual pain.[21] A report on married women with dysmenorrhea showed that 77 per cent were maladjusted sexually, whereas only 27 per cent of the control group were sexually maladjusted.

An exploratory study, done in connection with this research, found that women who had positive feelings about menstruation desired intercourse more frequently than those who had negative feelings about menstruation. There was a 34 per cent difference between the two groups; but since the numbers were small, this is not a statistically significant difference (Appendix D).

PREGNANCY AND INTERCOURSE

There is some evidence that sexual feelings also vary with pregnancy. Landis studied the rise and ebb of sexual desire during pregnancy in more than 200 couples by the questionnaire method. Although a few women reported increased desire during the beginning months of pregnancy, most tended to have less sexual desire as pregnancy progressed. Twenty-seven per cent of the women noticed a decrease in desire by the first three months of pregnancy, 43 per cent by the second three months of pregnancy, and 79 per cent by the last three months.

Absence of orgasm coupled with frequent undesired intercourse is reported to be related to nausea and vomiting in pregnancy. Robertson, who did the study, was in an unusually good position to obtain the information because he studied his own private obstetrical cases. He found that all of the pregnant women with severe nausea had disturbed sexual function, whereas only one in ten of the pregnant women without nausea had similar sexual problems.

An exploratory study, done in connection with this research, found that women who had positive feelings about pregnancy desired intercourse more frequently than those who had negative feelings about pregnancy. There was a 37 per cent difference between the two groups, but since the numbers were small this is not a statistically significant difference (see Appendix D).

CHILDBIRTH AND INTERCOURSE

There are some interesting similarities between the physiology of uninhibited, undrugged childbirth and the physiology of sexual excitement. The most strikingly similar points are as follows:

UNINHIBITED, UNDRUGGED CHILDBIRTH	SEXUAL EXCITEMENT
Breathing	
In the first stage of labor breathing becomes deeper during contractions	During early stages breathing becomes faster and deeper.
Second stage brings on very deep breaths with breath holding.	As orgasm approaches breathing becomes interrupted.
Tendency to make noises, grunts, etc.	Tendency to make gasping, sucking noises.
Facial Expression	
As delivery approaches face gets intense, strained look which makes observers often assume woman is suffering great pain.	As orgasm approaches face gets what Kinsey, *et al.* call a "tortured expression." Mouth open, glassy eyes, tense muscles.
Face looks like that of an athlete undergoing great physical strain.	Face looks like that of an athlete under great physical strain.
Uterus	
The upper segment of the uterus contracts rhythmically.	The upper segment of the uterus contracts rhythmically.
Loosening of mucus plug from os of cervix is one of the standard signs of labor.	Cervical secretion may loosen mucus plug which ordinarily lies at os of cervix thus opening it for spermatozoa.

Abdominal Muscles

Contract periodically. A strong, instinctive urge to bear down by using abdominal muscles as delivery approaches.

Abdominal muscles contract periodically with considerable force. Movement builds up as orgasm approaches.

Legs wide apart and bent.

This position is used by women in intercourse.

Central Nervous System

Woman becomes uninhibited particularly during second stage of labor. All veneer of "refinement" disappears.

Inhibitions and psychic blockages are relieved and often eliminated.

Delivery of the baby through the narrow passage calls for unusual strength and body expansion.

Unusual muscular strength. Many persons become capable of bending and distorting body in ways they could not otherwise do.

Sensory Perception

The vulva becomes anesthetic with full dilatation, so that woman often must be told of birth of baby's head.

Whole body of person who becomes sexually aroused becomes increasingly insensitive even to sharp blows and severe injury.

Amnesia, tendency to become insensitive to surroundings as delivery approaches.

As orgasm approaches loss of sensory perception is nearly complete —sometimes leading to moments of unconsciousness.

Suddenly, delivery completed, woman becomes wide awake.

After orgasm, sudden return of sensory acuity.

Emotional Response

After the birth of the baby there is a flood of joyful emotion. Read describes it as "complete and careless ecstasy."

There is a strong feeling of well being in most persons. Many psychologists believe that this relief from tension is the chief source of satisfaction gained from intercourse.

The sexual data for this comparison came almost entirely from Kinsey, *et al.* They base their statements not only on interviews with thousands of persons, but also on reports of scientifically trained persons observing human sexual activities, physiological experiments on human beings, and on evidence from other mammals.

The data on birth were gained chiefly from Grantly Dick Read, who has analyzed 516 consecutive labors. Read made every effort to keep women free from fear or disturbance, and thus uninhibited. Some of the birth data are corroborated by some movies and photographs of women in labor. Since in this country it is the custom to move, strap down, and otherwise disturb even undrugged women as they approach the birth climax, the behavior noted by Read may be not so frequent nor so pronounced here (see pages 39–40).

Feelings about childbirth may influence sexual adjustment. Landis, in his study of couples after the birth of their first child, found that those who did *not* fear childbirth had a higher proportion of very good sexual adjustment. Fewer of those who feared childbirth had very good sexual adjustments. The difference was statistically significant.

Landis's study done on 212 couples should be weighed much more heavily than the small exploratory study done in connection with this research which found no indication that feelings toward childbirth and feelings toward intercourse were related (Appendix D).

BREAST FEEDING AND INTERCOURSE

The function of the breast is closely related to the function of the other female organs. The breast develops about the time of the onset of menstruation and develops still further during pregnancy. Sexual excitement causes uterine contractions[3] and so does breast feeding.[6]

Uterine contractions during breast feeding are very sensitive to psychological stimuli. Experimental evidence indicates that this let-down reflex (which involves uterine contractions) does not occur when the mother is frightened or disturbed.[7,18]

The absence of uterine contractions may be a sign of breast feeding failure. Uterine contractions are easily noted in the early puerperium since they frequently cause pain to women in our society. Newton and Newton[8] asked mothers about these painful uterine contractions that occur *during* breast feeding. Mothers who went on to breast feed abundantly reported significantly more of such painful contractions than women who went on to have an inadequate milk supply. On the second day postpartum, 64 per cent of the successful breast feeders as opposed to 38 per cent of the unsuccessful breast feeders had painful uterine contractions during breast feeding.

The same hormone extract (Pitocin) that starts the let-down of milk is widely used to start the uterine contractions of labor. Oxytocin works both on breast and uterus. Although the let-down of milk is usually set off by the sucking of the baby, cows have been induced to let down their milk by stimulating their vulva or vagina.[9]

The breast and particularly the nipple are very sensitive organs. The nipple becomes erect on stimulation. Kinsey, et al. believe that about one out of every two women derives distinct satisfaction when the breast is involved in sexual play. They have records of some men and some women even reaching orgasm through breast stimulation.

Extensive breast stimulation occurs during breast feeding. The baby's mouth strokes the nipple for many minutes at a time. Often the little arm waves in an instinctive rhythmic motion, stroking the breast. When mother and baby are undressed they press firmly together, skin against skin. This kind of firm, continuous pressure is described by Kinsey, et al. as leading to sexual excitement.

Our culture makes every effort to minimize the possibilities of sensuous enjoyment of breast feeding. Usually the mother and baby are clothed and sucking time is limited. There is even an ingenious device called the nipple shield, whose purpose is to protect the nipple from the direct sucking of the baby. It can be found in almost every hospital. The popularity of manual expression of milk rather than letting the baby suck as much as it desires may also in part stem from this aversion to direct contact between mother and baby.

There is some evidence that breast feeding is somewhat of an antithesis of the menstruation-intercourse portion of woman's sexual cycle. Lactation delays ovulation and menstruation, and decreases the probability of conception (see page 52). Lactation of long duration causes the uterus to atrophy. The muscle fibers shrink from their enormous enlargement at the time of delivery to become smaller than their pre-pregnant state.[17]

Virtually all of the women included in this research study were lactating, and therefore might be expected to show evidence that their sexual energies were flowing into lactation. The exploratory study found that women who wanted to continue breast feeding said they desired less intercourse than women who planned to bottle feed. There was a 40 per cent difference between the two groups. Women who liked breast feeding also expressed less enjoyment in intercourse. There was a 27 per cent difference between the two groups. These differences, however, are not statistically significant since the numbers involved in the exploratory study were small (Appendix D).

MOTHERLINESS AND INTERCOURSE

Although religious institutions frequently emphasize that the enjoyment of sexual intercourse is for the purpose of procreation, this is frequently regarded as just a "moral" law. There is, however, some evidence that it may be also a psychological and physiological law for women, at least to some extent. Certainly intercourse behavior is related to many aspects of parenthood.

Sterility is related to sexual responsiveness in some instances. Wittkower and Wilson compared 30 sterile women with 30 women pregnant with their first babies. The sterile women had fertile husbands and no obvious abnormality of the genital tract. Eighty-seven per cent of the sterile women reported such difficulties as failure to have orgasm, no sexual feeling, pain during intercourse, painful vaginal spasm. Only 27 per cent of the control group reported similar troubles.

Parenthood may lead to lessened sexual desire. Landis in his study of 212 couples found that there was a significantly lower level of sex desire in both wives and husbands after the birth of their first child as compared with before the pregnancy. The relation between devaluation of motherhood and poor sexual adjustment is suggested in a study of 50 college women who expressed futility. Fifty-four per cent of these women did *not* have "being a good and successful mother" as *even one* of their major life goals, and 80 per cent expressed futility about sexual adjustment.[20]

The desire for children does not necessarily increase the orgasm rate of women. The Terman study on 556 selected women found no relation between orgasm and the conscious desire for children. Nor were number of children related to orgasm. However, fear of having children may be related to poor sexual adjustment. Landis found that wives who distrust their contraceptive methods reported a significantly lower rate of sexual adjustments than wives who did not distrust their contraceptive methods.

Marriage failure is highly related to lack of children. Popenoe quotes Alfred Cahen's calculations about the relation of divorce and childlessness. He concluded that there are about 71 chances in 100 that a childless couple will get a divorce. With one child the chances of divorce drop to 8 in 100, and every additional child cuts the statistical expectation of divorce in half again. The American Institute of Family Relations did a study of more than 8000 families in which the wife had passed childbearing age. There was a constant association between children and married happiness. Childless couples that remained undivorced in middle age were still less happy than families with children.

United States Census reports show that women married once have *more* children than women married two or more times.

The exploratory study of this research found no indication that positive feelings toward baby care and positive feelings toward intercourse were related (Appendix D). However, the main body of research did find that the mothers who liked looking after their babies also showed a slight tendency to marry younger than the less motherly women (Appendix D).

PRACTICAL APPLICATION

One of the most fundamental and well-demonstrated psychological laws states that the whole is *not* equal to the sum of its parts. For instance, a pencil drawing of an apple is not just a lot of pencil lines—it has a meaning over, above, and beyond those pencil lines. Similarly, women's sexuality can be viewed with more understanding if it is viewed as a whole rather than as disconnected parts.

One of the chief difficulties in viewing women's sexuality as a whole is that the taboos against some aspects of it are much greater than others. The intercourse aspect of women's sexuality is quite freely discussed in the popular press. The experiences of childbirth and pregnancy are just beginning to be freely discussed and even photographed. Equally frank talk about menstruation is still taboo, and the idea that successful breast feeding gives sensuous pleasure is generally considered utterly unprintable!

Another difficulty is that those women who use all the potentialities of their female bodies are the least likely to write, to speak, and to do research because they are absorbed in the task of growing children. Thus verbalization about women's sexuality tends to be left to men or to women who have rejected part of their female biological role.

The study of women's total sexuality is a great and fruitful area for future study. Women's wider sexual role forms the primitive basis of family life. Father and siblings have no bodily relationship between themselves. However, they share one common bond. All members of the family have had or do have a direct psychosomatic relationship with the mother. The problems of family life, the interactions of family life, and the satisfactions of family life cannot be fully understood without considering *all* aspects of these psychosomatic relationships.

SUMMARY

1. An exploratory study done in connection with this research yielded the suggestive finding that women who had the least desire for intercourse were more likely to have negative feelings toward menstruation and pregnancy, and to have positive feelings toward lactation.

2. Women's feelings toward intercourse may be closely related to every phase of her sexual role. Extensive controlled studies have found the following tendencies in certain groups of women:

A. Sexual desire and sexual activity waxes and wanes with the course of the menstrual cycle. Married women with severe menstrual pain are likely to be sexually maladjusted.

B. Pregnancy materially alters the sexual desires. Nausea and vomiting in pregnancy frequently are related to experiences of undesired intercourse.

C. Women who fear childbirth are less likely to have very good sexual adjustment. Uninhibited, undrugged childbirth is very similar to sexual excitement and orgasm in regard to the following points: Manner of breathing, facial expression, contractions of the uterus, contractions of the abdominal muscles, position of the body, reactions of the central nervous system, sensory perception, and emotional response.

D. Both breast feeding and sexual excitement cause uterine contractions. Women who fail to have uterine contractions during nursing are likely to have an insufficient milk supply. The breast is a very sensitive erotic area that gets extensive stimulation during breast feeding. The lactation portion of women's sexual cycle is physically somewhat the antithesis of the menstruation-intercourse portion of women's sexual cycle.

E. Marriages are happiest when the wife becomes a mother. Marriage failure is extremely frequent when the woman remains childless. Even if a childless woman remains undivorced till middle age, her marriage is likely to be unhappier than that of a similar woman who has become a mother.

3. In view of these findings, it seems reasonable to assume that women's response in intercourse can probably only be understood if the rest of her sexual role is fully considered as well.

REFERENCES

1. DOUGLAS, J. W. B.   The extent of breast feeding in Great Britain in 1946, with special reference to the health and survival of children. *J. Obst. & Gynaec. the Brit. Emp.* 57:335, 1950.
2. FARRIS, E. J.   *Human Fertility and Problems of the Male.*   White Plains, N. Y., Author's Press, 1950.
3. KINSEY, A. C., *et al. Sexual Behavior in the Human Female.*   Philadelphia, Saunders, 1953.
4. LANDIS, J. T.   The effects of first pregnancy upon the sexual adjustment of 212 couples. *Am. Soc. Rev. 15:*767, 1950.
5. McCANCE, R. A., *et al.*   Physical and emotional periodicity in women. *J. Hyg.* 37:571, 1937.

6. MOIR, CHASSAR   Recording the contractions of the human pregnant and non-pregnant uterus. *Tr. Edinburgh Obst. Soc. 54:*93, 1934.
7. NEWTON, M., and NEWTON, NILES   The let-down reflex in human lactation. *J. Pediat. 33:*698, 1948.
8. NEWTON, NILES, and NEWTON, M.   Relation of the let-down reflex to ability to breast feed. *Pediatrics 5:*726, 1950.
9. NÜESCH, A.   Uber das sogenannte Aufziehen der Milch bei der Kuh. Inaug. Diss. Zürich, 1904. As cited by Hammond, J. *Veterinary Rec. 16:*519, 1936.
10. POPENOE, P.   Infertility and the stability of marriage. *Western J. Surg. 56:*309, 1948.
11. READ, G. D.   *Childbirth Without Fear.*   New York, Harper & Brothers, 1944.
12. READ, G. D.   The discomforts of childbirth. *Brit. M. J. 1:*651, 1949.
13. READ, G. D.   Observations on a series of labors with special reference to physiological delivery. *Lancet 1:*721, 1949.
14. READ, G. D.   *The Birth of a Child.*   New York, Vanguard, 1950.
15. READ, G. D.   *Introduction to Motherhood.*   New York, Harper & Brothers, 1950.
16. ROBERTSON, G. G.   Nausea and vomiting in pregnancy. *Lancet 2:*336, 1946.
17. SANGER, M.   Die Ruckbildung der Muscularis des Puerperalen Uterus. *Beitr. z. path., Anat. u. Klin. med. von Wagner's Schülen,* 1887, p. 134. quoted by Beck, A. C. *Obstetrical Practice* (2 Ed.). Baltimore, Williams and Wilkins, 1939.
18. STEERE.   Discussion of paper by Moir, C.[6]
19. TERMAN, L. M.   Correlates of orgasm adequacy in a group of 556 wives. *J. Psychol. 32:*115, 1951.
20. WILSON, PAULINE   *College Women Who Express Futility.* New York, Bureau of Publications, Teacher's College, Columbia University, 1950.
21. WITTKOWER, E., and WILSON, A. T. M.   Dysmenorrhea and sterility. *Brit. M. J. 2:*586, 1940.

CHAPTER 10

BIOLOGICAL FEMININITY VERSUS CULTURAL FEMININITY

THE THEORY OF BIOLOGICAL FEMININITY AND THE FACTS UPON WHICH IT IS BASED

WOMEN'S STATUS IN WESTERN HISTORY

A favorite cliché of modern writing and thinking is the assumption that women have just recently won status and personal rights. Mary Beard has tested this belief against the facts. She finds the belief that women have just emerged from a subjugation which dates back to pre-historic times is contrary to some historical documents. For instance, Roman civil law provided for equality of husband and wife in the marriage partnership. During the early period of English history land was inherited directly through women, and some women were leaving their husbands and "taking" their land and children with them. An analysis of 85 English medieval guilds showed that 72 admitted women as members *on an equal basis with men.* Evidently the women were very outspoken at guild meetings, for the by-laws provide that the "sistern" no less than the "bretheren" must keep the peace and avoid disorderly debates.

Beard points out that as modern states emerged after the Middle Ages, queens and women of the ruling aristocracy had a great influence on the affairs of state both directly and indirectly until the eighteenth century, when the power of the aristocracy was broken. Meanwhile, in rural families husband and wife worked together, each having heavy respon-sibilities for field and household. When the husband was away at war, as he frequently was, the wife assumed full management of both the land and the household.

The reader may ask: "How can anything so popular as this belief in the subjugation of women be a fallacy?" Beard traces the origins of the fallacy to Blackstone's misinterpretations of English law. This was seized upon by feminists to show that women were indeed badly used. The public has not been disabused of the idea since historians may tend to write about only the frivolous side of female historical figures, or may ignore them completely. For instance, an analysis of some books covering early American history by historians indicates that great American women who are known to have played a real part in the history of the period have been generally ignored.[1] Another example is Cleopatra, whose "sex appeal" has become famous. Actually the documents of her history show that she was not especially beautiful, but highly educated, a skilled organizer, and a woman of business.[2]

WOMEN'S LOSSES IN RECENT YEARS

The modern era has actually lowered the position of women by robbing them of the responsibilities which they normally held within the institution of the family, as Lundberg and Farnham have pointed out in their perceptive book on women.

Their first loss was in the economic realm. Women lost part of their usefulness when the home ceased to be the central productive unit of society. Previously most of the needs of the family were met by home manufacture, and women had their full share of responsibility for this. They also helped produce what was sold outside of the home.

With the coming of the industrial and commercial revolutions, most productive work moved outside the home. Income became more and more important as fewer and fewer of the material needs of the family were provided by home production. Women tended to become more dependent on their husbands because his work and income became the chief source of livelihood for the whole family.

Today less than three out of ten women are considered "gainful workers" by the United States Census Bureau. Only about 29 per cent of American women over 14 were classified as gainful workers in 1950. Thus 71 per cent of modern American women do not have the solid satisfaction that comes from doing work that is recognized as economically useful. Even among women aged 18 to 24—when women's employment is at its height—less than 45 per cent are considered "gainful workers."

The second great loss came in the devaluation of women's motherly role. As work moved out of the home, children—like women—became economic liabilities because they could not help with production. The birth rate fell and there were fewer children to care for.

Women's childbearing and child care role has been greatly minimized in the last 150 years. United States Census reports[6] going back to 1800 show the ratio of white women between the ages of 20 and 44 to the number of white children under 5. They indicate the following facts: In 1800 and 1810 there were more than 1300 children for every 1000 women. By 1820 this ratio started to fall, and by 1850 there were only about 900 children for every 1000 women. In 1900 there were less than 700 children for every 1000 women. In 1940 the number of children had dropped to nearly 400. However, since then the birth rate has climbed again to near 1915 levels, and the number of children to women has probably increased to around 600 children to 1000 women. Thus a conservative estimate indicates that women's childbearing and child care role has been lessened by at least 50 per cent since the industrial revolution.

Not only do women of childbearing age have fewer children under 5, but their teaching responsibilities for older children are greatly lessened. In the home-production era of society, women used to teach their older children the arts of home production, homemaking, and child care. Public school was a relatively small factor in the life of the older child.[5] In 1870 only 57 per cent of the children between 5 and 17 attended public school, and they attended on the average of only 78 days per year. In 1949 79 per cent of the children between 5 and 17 attended public school, and each child attended for an average of 156 days. This means that the modern woman has less responsibility for her older children. Again, she is less needed and less useful than she was previously.

Women's economic productiveness seems to be closely linked with their motherly role. Rural farm women still, to some extent, live in the home-production stage of society. They, more than urban women, help produce the source of family income and/or produce the products the family uses or eats. Farm women, along with this extra work, are more apt to be mothers. Only 9 per cent of rural farm women who have ever been married are childless—as compared with 19 per cent of similar women living in large cities.[5] Rural farm women on the average produce almost twice as many children as women who live in large cities. Their children attend school for about three years less time.[5]

It is not surprising to find that as women became less useful in the home the divorce rate should begin to rise. The divorce rate began to climb around 1880.[6] By 1900 it was more than twice as high as in 1879. By 1940 it was more than six times as high as 1879. In 1945, with war marriages breaking up, it was more than eleven times as high as 1879. In 1949 it was still nine times as high as 1879.[5] Thus a woman today is about nine times as likely to have her marriage terminated by divorce as a woman of seventy years ago.

CULTURAL FEMININITY AND ITS SOURCES

As the productive, educational, and childbearing functions of the home have become greatly minimized, the active, productive, motherly type of woman has become a misfit within the home. However, if she leaves the home she goes from an environment where she has equality with men into an environment where she meets serious discriminations—which have already been discussed in Chapter 8.

Not only does she experience discrimination outside the home, but success in her work outside the home is punished by even greater denial of her female biological role. A very successful woman is less apt to have children and is less desirable to men. Specific evidence for this point is furnished by the *Fortune* Survey. The majority of men with opinions said that men would prefer to marry girls who had been only moderately successful or who had never worked. Only about one in five men said men would choose to marry the woman who had been extremely successful at a job even though she was just as beautiful as other women. Women feel this discrimination. The *Fortune* Survey shows that even more women than men believed the men would choose the less successful girl.

In the realm of exceptionally successful women this tendency becomes extreme. Forty per cent of women in *Who's Who* report no marriage, and 41 per cent of those ever married and past the childbearing age report no children.[3]

The effects of recent changes in society, therefore, may have tended to emphasize feelings of inferiority, envy, and dependence, and to have encouraged negative feelings toward childbearing. Most women in our society might be expected to have these feelings. They would be a basic part of their psychology—or "cultural femininity."

BIOLOGICAL FEMININITY AND ITS SOURCES

There would be no harm in society's putting a premium on inactive, dependent behavior in women if they were by nature built to be this way. However, the female biological role is far from passive and unproductive. In fact, the woman who is adequate in her female biological role must be active, productive, and capable of concerted effort.

There is no harder physical exertion than normal childbirth. Developing and carrying a baby through pregnancy is an active process, and breast feeding a baby involves repeated active giving. The adequate care of a baby involves constant and, if need be, aggressive protection of the baby from injury and working to meet its needs. The good mother does not just sit passively comforting the child; she strives to separate the child from the offending object—be it a cherry pit in the trachea, a sadistic teacher, or housing that does not permit normal exercise.

Evidence we have from animals confirms the view that biological femininity is the opposite from passivity. Foresters report that a bull moose in mating season is less dangerous than a cow moose with her new calf. Anyone who has had a chance to become familiar with farm life knows how aggressive even domestic animal mothers can be if they feel their offspring is endangered. There is also confirmation of these observations in the controlled experiments of Warden. He found that a rat mother will overcome much more resistance to get to her young than a sex-deprived male animal will overcome to get to a female. The rat mothers struggled harder to get to their babies than they struggled to get to food or water, no matter how hungry or thirsty they were.

TESTING THE BIOLOGICAL FEMININITY THEORY AGAINST FACTS

It is thus apparent that the characteristics of women or their femininity may be classified in two groups. One is developed by biological factors and may be termed biological femininity, and the other is developed by cultural factors and may be termed cultural femininity. Since the industrial revolution there has been a sharper conflict between these two.

An exploratory study was done in an attempt to begin to test this theory. Terman's M-F Test was administered to some of the research group as a method of measuring cultural femininity. Since the numbers tested were small and somewhat unrepresentative of the total research group, the results should be most cautiously interpreted.

The results, however, are in line with the theory that biological femininity is indeed something *different from* cultural femininity—and *in some ways opposite to* cultural femininity. The culturally feminine women in this study showed no greater liking for menstruation, childbirth, or breast feeding, but were more likely to feel satisfied by women's role in modern society. They definitely tended to dislike pregnancy. Furthermore, the culturally feminine women were extremely likely to wish to be men. This last relationship was so great that it was statistically significant ($p<0.04$) in spite of the small number of women studied (Appendix D).

These findings suggest that there may indeed be a valid distinction between cultural and biological femininity. More research is needed.

PRACTICAL APPLICATIONS

It is popular to think about women's problems and psychology only in the light of modern society. Thus woman's motherly role, and her historical role in home production, are apt to be overlooked—for these are greatly minimized by our culture. Further research and thought about women's psychology and women's problems should recognize that their biological and cultural roles may be quite different from each other, and in some ways in conflict.

SUMMARY

1. Contrary to popular belief, women have lost status rather than gained status with the coming of the industrial revolution. When production moved out of the home, women became more dependent on their husbands' support. Women's childbearing and child care contribution to society became depreciated as children became economic burdens and the birth rate fell. Women's usefulness as teachers and supervisors of their own older children was greatly minimized as schools consumed more and more of the children's time. After women became less needed and important to family life, the divorce rate began to rise.

2. These changes made feelings of insecurity, inferiority, envy, and dependence part of the accepted feminine pattern. Actions which stem from such feelings are considered culturally feminine.

3. On the other hand, biological pressures put a premium on productiveness, activity, concerted effort, and aggressiveness in women. These biologically feminine characteristics are often opposite from those encouraged by our society.

4. An exploratory study was set up to begin to test this reasoning. The most culturally feminine women almost always showed deep feelings of inferiority by saying they wished to be men; the least culturally feminine women very seldom felt so inferior that they said they wished to be men.

REFERENCES

1. BEARD, MARY R. *Woman as a Force in History.* New York, Macmillan, 1946.
2. Fortune Survey *Fortune 34:5* (Aug.), 1946.
3. KISER, C. V., and SCHACTER, N. L.   Demographic characteristics of women in *Who's Who. Milbank Mem. Fund Quart. 27:*392, 1949.
4. LUNDBERG, F., and FARNHAM, M. F. *Modern Woman: The Lost Sex.* New York, Harper & Brothers, 1947.
5. United States Bureau of Census *Statistical Abstract of the United States 1952 (ed. 73)* Washington, D. C., Government Printing Office, 1952.
6. United States Bureau of Census *Historical Statistics of the United States 1789–1945.* Washington, D. C., Government Printing Office, 1949.
7. WARDEN, C. J. *Animal Motivation Studies: The Albino Rat.* New York, Columbia Univ. Press, 1931. (Cited by Munn, N. L. *Psychology: The Fundamentals of Human Adjustment.* Boston, Houghton, 1946.)

CHAPTER 11

CONCLUSIONS

The reader is referred to the summaries at the end of each of the preceding chapters, starting on pages 4, 12, 21, 29, 40, 56, 70, 83, 92 and 100. These summaries contain some concluding remarks.

The basic finding of this book is that women's feelings toward menstruation, pregnancy, childbirth, breast feeding, baby care, and envy of men are important and should not be ignored by those who wish to understand and help women. These feelings of women are important because they are related to many other aspects of their lives.

Although the findings of this particular research study are suggestive, the case for the importance of women's feelings toward their biologically determined role rests on a much broader base. Experimental and statistical studies done by many different investigators, under many different circumstances, on many different types of women, have been cited. They almost all tend to show the same general thing—that woman's feelings and emotions toward her wider sexual role are often related to her behavior, her attitudes, and her health. In general, but not always, positive feelings are more likely to be associated with good health and well-being, whereas negative feelings are more likely to be associated with poor health and dissatisfaction.

Our present state of knowledge permits no more detailed conclusions. However, statistical and experimental facts from this research and from others suggest the following *possibilities:*

1. Women who complain about menstruation are more likely to esteem masculinity, to be unmotherly, and to have more obstetrical and gynecological problems. Women's moods and feelings and activities are

102

to some extent related to the course of their menstrual cycle. Also, conversely, menstrual flow, menstrual regularity, and menstrual pain are sometimes influenced by women's feelings.

2. Women who complain about pregnancy are more likely to wish to be men and to have fewer motherly desires. Their pregnancies are more apt to be terminated by easy deliveries. The majority of women in our society dislike being pregnant during the early months of pregnancy, but become reconciled to the baby as its arrival approaches.

3. Women who feel childbirth is "hard" are less likely to express physical affection for their babies. They are more likely to have fewer children and to dislike breast feeding and baby care. Unfortunate experiences in childbirth may give psychological trauma of the severest sort. The course of labor can be influenced by psychological factors.

4. Women who do not wholeheartedly desire to breast feed are less likely to be motherly individuals—both physically and psychologically. They are apt to feel that childbirth is hard; and, if primiparas, may have longer labors. Attempts to breast feed in such women lead to less secretion of milk. Women who reject breast feeding are more apt to feel men have a more satisfying time in life, and are more likely to reject children. Breast feeding failure is closely related to women's emotions.

5. Women who dislike caring for their newborn babies are also more likely to dislike most other aspects of their female biological role. As a group the physical functioning of their genital tract is less efficient and they have fewer children. The physical course of menstruation may be particularly closely related to maternal behavior.

6. Women's experiences in sexual intercourse are related to their feeling and experiences in the realm of menstruation, pregnancy, childbirth, breast feeding, and motherhood.

7. Women who envy men are more likely to desire boy babies and to dislike some aspects of women's biological role. However, they are apt to be unusually adequate in some portions of their reproductive role and to have faith in women's abilities. Women's desire to be men is related to certain social factors.

8. Modern trends in society have greatly reduced women's motherly and productive responsibilities within the home. At the same time, women are still experiencing discrimination when working outside of the home. These facts are important to female psychology since they may push women toward unmotherliness and dependence, whereas women's biological role calls for activity and productiveness. This may lead to two types of femininity which are different and partly opposed to one another.

Thus many aspects of social and physical well-being tend to be related to women's feelings about menstruation, pregnancy, childbirth, breast feeding, infant care, and envy of men. Women's feelings in this area are probably of real importance to physicians, psychologists, social workers, marriage counselors, and other professional groups dealing with women. Last but not least, women's feelings about this intimate portion of their lives are of considerable importance to women themselves and to their husbands and children.

APPENDIX A

WAYS OF ENCOURAGING THE EXPRESSION OF
PERSONAL FEELINGS

What can be done to encourage the expression of intimate feelings in a setting where they can be observed by others? Unfortunately, the answer to this question still lies more in the realm of opinion and individual experience than in the realm of objectively tested knowledge. The following discussion states the beliefs of this investigator and how she applied them in this research. To check the validity of her methods, she compared some data obtained by her methods with data collected from other sources. There was a high rate of agreement between the two sources of information (see Appendix B, pages 121–122).

AN APPROPRIATE TIME

Picking an appropriate time is an important part of encouraging free and full expression of feelings. Leisure and freedom from immediate needs for action are most conducive to the expression of feelings. Thus one may learn more about the basic feelings of a stranger with whom one shares a double seat of a day coach for several hours than one may learn from months of working with a colleague in a busy office.

Pain, strong emotion, or anxiety tend to crowd out other more subtle feelings and make them difficult to assess. The patient who has just been told she must have an operation is in no mood to talk about her personal feelings on some unrelated subject. Nor can a mother be very expressive when she must watch a two-year-old in a room full of breakables. Such situations might give good indications of how the patient feels about her operation, or the mother about her child, but not about other aspects of their feelings.

Some situations are particularly favorable to the expression of feelings. Women after childbirth may be in one of these favorable states. Margaret Fries, who has done considerable work with mothers and newborn babies,

105

observes: ". . . Mothers are generally eager to talk at this time. Delivery and nursing the infant act as a natural stimuli for free associations. Thus the doctor without psychiatric training can readily obtain much information which helps him to understand the case."[1]

Using an Appropriate Time in this Research

The mothers used in this research were singularly free from immediate outside pressures or duties. They had little to do other than eat, sleep, visit, and care for their babies. Excessive pain and worry were to some extent ruled out, since only mothers in relatively good health with reasonably healthy babies were included in the research.

In my opinion, the atmosphere of the ward was unusually peaceful, thus being very conducive to the free expression of feelings. In spite of the several babies and mothers sharing the same room, there was little disturbing crying to be heard. Only once in the months I worked there did I hear a baby crying in the loud, uncontrolled manner so typical of hospital nurseries. That crying came from an illegitimate baby whose mother wanted to give it up for adoption. Walking through the wards one usually saw scenes of mothers quietly sitting in rocking chairs or snoozing with babies at their breast.

ENVIRONMENTAL SETTING

Environmental setting can be a potent force in encouraging or discouraging the free expression of feeling. Society allows the intimate expression of feelings in certain surroundings, and using the aura of these surroundings can be a great aid in encouraging the expression of feelings. Students who have a warm relationship with their teachers can actually enjoy writing voluntary autobiographies expressing feelings and emotions so deep that they would hesitate to share them with their closest friends. A woman in a gynecologist's office may answer freely questions that she might consider very offensive if asked by her neighbor or even, perhaps, by a psychologist.

The Environmental Setting in this Research

This research study tried to make full use of the medical setting to encourage the expression of intimate feelings. Interviews were done in the hospital, at the bedside of the patient—with curtains drawn to give a sense of privacy. The interviewer called herself "Dr. Newton," and wore a white gown.

At the same time these research data were being collected, another study was also being done on the subject of nipple pain and nipple damage.[2] This involved asking questions about pain and the amount of sucking the child did, and meant examining the nipple for signs of physical trauma. This procedure led naturally into the first question of this research study which was about feelings toward breast feeding. The interviewer was a familiar sight in the wards, as the nipple pain study involved examining almost every mother almost every day. Thus the approach to the patient was gradual and through a medical field of inquiry.

RAPPORT

A mutual feeling of respect, trust, and good will is perhaps the most important of all in establishing the free expression of feelings. The building of the rapport is primarily the job of the investigator. If his life experiences have made him afraid of being shunned or hurt by other people, he is unlikely to be able to establish a warm relationship with people easily. If he feels that women or Negroes or other segments of society are somehow fundamentally different from himself, the feeling of mutual respect and good will will be lacking. If he has had similar enough experiences so that he can *feel with* the people he talks to, that is a big step toward good rapport.

Some Problems in Establishing Rapport

The establishment of good feelings between the interviewer and the subject involves more than the lack of interfering factors. It is an active, changing sort of relationship that requires using all the knowledge of the subtleties of human interactions acquired from years of harmonious living with other people. Establishing such a good relationship with a person one does not know requires giving a great deal of concentrated effort—it can be very fatiguing. This may be a real limiting factor in the number of interviews that can be well done in the same day.

Nothing kills good rapport quicker than a dissecting, analyzing, or moralizing frame of mind. Eagerness to label, judge, or diagnose the feeling may give the investigator a feeling of safety or satisfaction; but it hinders the free and full expression of feeling. Almost no one likes to feel he is being dissected or judged; yet almost every normal individual begins to feel comfortable and relaxed when he talks to a person who shows interest in and kindly understanding of his feelings.

Unfortunately, good rapport is sometimes thought of as establishing a relationship in which the subject tells the investigator what he expects and wants to hear. If the investigator has some preconceived theory, he may not consider rapport really good until the subject spurts forth the evidence to validate his theories. For instance, if he believes that all women suffer from penis envy so deep that it is the main motivating force of their lives, he is apt to feel that the woman who fails to give enough evidence of this feeling is "resistant." Actually, if he approached the problem with the idea . . . "Here is a unique individual—her feelings toward herself and other human beings are important— What are these feelings?" . . . he might find that he could obtain a wealth of information about many important feelings of her life.

The physician who through many years of training has been taught to refer to the uterine contractions of the birth process as "pains" is in a similar sort of position. He is likely to believe that the occasional woman who insists that her strong uterine contractions are not painful is just a stoic and is hiding her real feelings.

There is considerable controversy about how long a period of personal contact between individuals is necessary to induce the free expression of feelings. Attempts to *change* feelings may take much more time than getting feelings expressed.

Also, since the wealth of feeling is so great it takes time to express the *details* of feelings. Take the example of a woman who is so much in favor of breast feeding that she breast fed all four of her children abundantly for many months. Prolonged interview would give her time to express the petty annoyances that she felt accompanied breast feeding. Her main, overwhelming feeling of liking for breast feeding would usually have been shown much sooner by her actions as well as by an account of her feelings in this regard.

I personally believe that a feeling of mutual respect, trust, and good will can be built up in a surprisingly short time with normal individuals. Many of the main feelings of the individual can be quickly observed within this framework of good rapport, provided one is not misled by interpreting the symptoms of feeling too literally. After all, showing one's feelings is the easiest thing to do! A baby has no inhibitions about showing his emotions, and attempts to hide feelings are only learned with difficulty throughout childhood.

FEELINGS OF RAPPORT INVOLVED IN THIS RESEARCH

Although judgments of oneself as an interviewer are bound to contain personal bias, it is perhaps worthwhile noting a few points about my feelings concerning the interview. As a research worker interested in the whole field of women's feelings, what these mothers had to say seemed to me to be very important. As a mother of two young children myself, I felt a deep bond of common experience with the mothers I talked to. I also happen to like babies, and I suppose my feeling toward them was quite evident from my frequent smiles. Certainly interested remarks about the baby was a good fulcrum for building rapport with most mothers.

The general attitude of the mothers appeared to be one of interest and cooperation. With little to do except rest, sleep, and feed and change their babies, the diversion of the interview with its chance to talk about their very immediate and real experiences was welcome. Records made immediately after the interview indicate that 145, or 77 per cent, of the interviews were conducted with "good" rapport, in my opinion. Most of the other interviews were deemed "fair." This meant that the mothers were quite reserved, or that the rapport varied from one part of the interview to the other. Only three were considered "poor" throughout.

In comparing the types of feelings elicited in "good" interviews as compared with "fair" and "poor" interviews, it was found that negative feelings about pregnancy were voiced significantly ($p < 0.02$) more frequently when "good" rapport existed. The pregnancy question came early in the interview at just that point when it became apparent that the interview would cover more than breast feeding. The interview with "fair" rapport was often poor around this time, developing to better rapport later on. More significant differences would probably have been found had there been more "poor" interviews, since the "fair" interviews were like the "good" ones in many ways.

The level of cooperation of the mothers can also be seen in the number willing to take the time and trouble to fill out the M-F test. The test consisted of 456 items to be answered, and no appeal was made to self-interest at the time the test was requested by promising to give results. Yet 41 of the 71 mothers asked completed the lengthy test.

UNBIASED QUESTIONING

Asking unbiased questions that encourage the expression of feelings is another important point in technique. Particular care must be taken when, for the sake of collecting a lot of comparable data, specific questions must be asked repeatedly.

The first step in the process is to become thoroughly familiar with the type of feelings that may exist and with the way they are expressed in the group to be studied. This can be learned by a more casual type of questioning.

The second step involves learning how to phrase questions in such a way that they will neither suggest feelings that do not exist, nor cut off the expression of feelings by a mere yes or no answer.

Next, if a standardized wording of questions is desired for research purposes, the wording of the questions must be tested again and again on the same sort of persons that will be studied in the final research. Continuous revisions must be done on the basis of these findings. The purpose of this is to make sure that the final questions really do elicit the expression of a wide range of feeling in the area to be studied.

How the Questions Used in this Research were Developed

Numerous women were interviewed before the questionnaire used in this study was put into its final form. The first acquaintance with the mothers came through the collecting of data for the nipple pain and nipple damage research.[2] Then the conversations naturally began to branch out to other subjects. Finally the first tentative questionnaire was written down and tried. This questionnaire went through four revisions and was tested on 56 mothers before it was put in final form.

In testing suitable inquiries, direct, straightforward questions were usually tried first. These usually proved to be satisfactory with minor changes in wording. However, the question "Would you like more children?" had to be changed to the more indirect one of "What do you think the ideal size for the family is—how many children?" because the first form of the question brought so many requests for contraceptive information which the interviewer was not prepared to give. A direct question about pleasure in the baby was not tried, but the more indirect one about satisfaction with the sex of the baby was used even during the preliminary interviews in the belief that direct questioning might be offensive to the mother. In retrospect the investigator feels that direct questioning about attitude toward the baby itself would have been more effective. A more useful question would probably have been something like this: "Were you pleased with your baby or a little disappointed at first?"

STANDARDIZED QUESTIONS USED IN THIS RESEARCH

The interview blank in its final form looked like this:

1. How would you like to feed your baby when you get out of the hospital?

_____

_____

    Would you like to breast feed or bottle feed your baby? _____

    Any particular reason you feel that way? _____

    How long would you like to nurse your baby? _____

_____

2. How did you feel during your pregnancy?

_____

_____

    Did you ever have an upset stomach or vomiting? _____

_____

3. Before you got pregnant, how did you feel during your menstrual periods?

_____

_____

    Did you ever have any pain or other discomfort? _____

4. Did you have a hard time or did you have an easy time giving birth to this baby?

_____

_____

_____

_____

_____

5. Are you pleased you have a little _____ or would you rather have a little _____?

_____
_____
_____
_____
_____

6. Do you think men or do you think women have a more satisfying time in life?

_____
_____

    Is there any particular reason you feel that way? _____

_____
_____
_____

7. A lot of women have told me they sometimes wished they were a man. Have you ever wished you were a man? _____

_____
_____
_____
_____

8. How do you feel about having the baby in the same room with you here in the hospital? _____

_____
_____

    Is there any particular reason you feel that way? _____

_____
_____
_____

9. Did you have your last baby at home or in the hospital? Home _____ Hospital _____ At the hospital was the baby kept in the nursery or was it in the same room with you? _____

10. What do you think is the ideal size for a family—how many children?

_____
_____
_____
_____
_____

11. Did you ever read or hear about relaxing as a way of stopping the pain of childbirth? _____

_____

_____

      Did you try relaxing? _____

      Do you feel it helped you? _____

_____

_____

12. Did you attend the mother's classes? Yes _____ No _____

The indented questions in sections 2, 3, 6 and 8 were asked only when the information was not volunteered in answer to the previous questions. The question "Would you like to breast feed or bottle feed your baby?" was used when the mother responded to the first feeding question with a reply about feeding schedules or otherwise indicated misunderstanding. The question "Any particular reason you feel that way?" was used when the mother indicated a desire to bottle feed in part or entirely. The question "How long would you like to nurse your baby?" was used when the mother indicated she wished to breast feed her baby partly or entirely. The sex of the baby was inserted in the first blank space in section 5 and the opposite sex was inserted in the other blank space.

During the process of collecting the data, but before they had been evaluated in any way, the investigator came to realize that further information about feelings would be useful. Therefore some mothers were asked about their work history and a few were given masculinity-femininity tests and asked about their feelings toward sexual intercourse. These added data were considered purely exploratory in nature.

REFERENCES

1. FRIES, MARGARET Interrelated factors in development. *Am. J. Orthopsychiat. 8:*726, 1938.
2. NEWTON, NILES Nipple pain and nipple damage. *J. Pediat. 41:*411, 1952.

APPENDIX B

THE INTERPRETATION AND MEASUREMENT OF
PERSONAL FEELINGS

The study of human feelings presents two major problems. The first, which was discussed in Appendix A, is the problem of how to get feelings and emotions expressed in such a way that they can be observed. The second problem, an equally important one, is how to interpret and measure these often oblique signs of emotions in an unbiased manner. The following account describes the methods used by this investigator and the theories behind this choice of methods. There is great need for more objective research on this problem, and undoubtedly fifty years hence the thinking and methods used in our era will seem very crude indeed.

SOME FACTORS THAT BIAS JUDGMENT

Unfortunately, many other factors besides the actual symptoms of feeling determine how we interpret them. Suppose a good friend walks past us without saying hello or taking note of us. If our fiancée has just broken the engagement, or if we regard ourself as fundamentally quite unlikable, we are apt to interpret the act as a sign of disdain. If we come from a near-sighted family, we may see no emotional symptom at all but merely wonder if the man needs stronger glasses. If we are a psychologist trained in Cameron's biosocial interpretation of behavior we may take note of the incident as an example of behavioral overexclusion,[2] while if we are psychoanalytically orientated we will speculate about deep unconscious motivations.

RESEARCH EVIDENCE SHOWING HUMAN TENDENCIES TOWARD BIAS

Many experiments demonstrate that judgments are influenced by what we expect to see or believe we should see.[1, 3] When a person is asked to draw a figure he is shown momentarily, he tends to draw what he expects

113

to see. If the figure O–O is flashed before him, and he expects to see spectacles, he draws something that looks like spectacles. Whereas if exactly the same figure is shown him but he expects to see an athletic dumbbell, he draws something that looks like a dumbbell.

The influence of the opinion of others may have a subtle and far-reaching effect on judgments. One way this has been demonstrated is by leading a group of persons in a strange dark room with only one tiny visible point of light. It is actually stationary, but it seems to waver in the darkness. When a member of the group is asked how far the light is moving and in what direction, he tends to give the same sort of estimate that he has heard others give before him. Even when later tested alone about the distance of the light and its direction of movement, his judgments tend to stay very similar to the judgment previously expressed by the group as a whole.

Complex judgments seem to follow the same pattern. Many individuals were asked to estimate the beauty of some pictures. They judged the pictures more beautiful when they were attributed to a famous artist than when exactly the same pictures were attributed to an obscure artist. Such biased judgment occurs all the time in daily living. Consider two partisan fans watching a championship boxing match. The boxers are well matched and both are fighting in their best form. The fan of Boxer A is sure his man is the hardest hitter, while the fan of Boxer B is equally convinced his favorite is clearly the best.

TYPES OF BIAS THAT INFLUENCE JUDGMENT

The existence of bias in estimating the feelings of others is no cause for despair. Just as a good referee can eliminate most of the bias from his boxing match decisions, so a person can learn to interpret the feelings of others more and more accurately. He can learn to recognize his own tendency toward bias and thus help to discount its influence over his judgment.

There are several types of bias that are constantly with us all. One is an emotional-physical bias. The second comes from family and social relationships. Another comes from overapplication of preconceived theories and interpretations.

The emotional-physical bias is a strong one. The marriage counselor who rushes to the office on a drizzly morning after a sleepless night without taking time to eat may be inclined to believe a couple presents a hopeless emotional problem; whereas on a bright spring day, after a good sleep and a good breakfast, the same couple acting the same way might seem to him to show no insoluble emotional incompatibility. Likewise, the physician who dislikes the hospital administration may overinterpret the patient's feelings about inadequacies of the hospital care.

Family and social relationships may be surprisingly potent in influencing professional judgment. The obstetrician whose own wife welcomes heavy sedation and unconscious delivery may often misgage the feelings of a woman who asks for natural childbirth—with the results that he may not give her the cooperation she needs. The pediatrician whose own children were abundantly breast fed may not easily interpret the signs of resentment of some of his patients when he insists they keep on trying to breast feed.

Another sort of bias derives from overapplication of some interpretations to the exclusion of others. For instance, modern scholastic thinking places a heavy emphasis on the dangers of pushing a child too hard and emphasizes that misbehavior in the classroom may be due to unfavorable emotional influences at home. Divorced parents are apt to be blamed for the obviously disruptive symptoms of a boy who insists on continuously and uncontrollably disturbing classwork by whispering loudly, throwing spit balls, and passing notes. Often enough this interpretation may be true, but preconceived theories may prevent the teacher from even considering the real possibility that the boy is bright and that his symptoms may originate in boredom with unchallenging school work.

AVOIDING BIAS WHEN JUDGING PERSONAL FEELINGS

Simple awareness of possible prejudices can do much to discount the effect of biasing judgment. The marriage counselor who recognizes that his physical state may be leading him to be unduly pessimistic may handle his case in a different way from the man who takes his feelings of depression completely seriously. The obstetrician or pediatrician who is willing to admit to himself that his family life *does* influence his understanding of his patients' feelings may more easily keep this influence from doing harm. The teacher who is willing to consider boredom as well as emotional instability as a cause of obstreperous behavior may help more children.

Blind spots in interpreting the signs of feelings can be partly avoided by vigilant awareness that such blindness exists. Awareness of one's own emotions, prejudices, and feelings is of fundamental importance. Such self-understanding, like most other mental qualities, can be developed and trained. It can be taught to normal people in the course of school and professional training, and it should be taught there. The awareness of *all* possible interpretations of the signs of feeling is also teachable. Great teachers regularly stimulate their students to think beyond the narrow confines of fashionable thought.

However, in spite of the precautions that can minimize bias, it is obvious that for scientific research purposes "intuitive" judgment of feeling must be carefully controlled. One method of doing this is to make objective records of the symptoms of feeling and then have independent judges, who know nothing about the person whose symptoms are being studied, judge the data. Such an independent judge does not, of course, have access to all the subtle clues that might help to form the diagnosis of the original collector of the data; but his judgment is relatively free from biases and preconceived ideas that might influence decisions. Thus the point of view being tested has a fair chance of being disproved.

METHODS USED IN THIS RESEARCH FOR INTERPRETING AND MEASURING PERSONAL FEELINGS

FINDING THE PATTERNS OF REPLY

After the 190 cases had been interviewed using the final version of the interview form, the replies were minutely inspected in order to find trends or types of answers given in response to each question. In the answer to some questions it was possible to find five distinct categories of verbal response ranging from very positive to very negative feeling; while in the responses to other questions only two or three patterns of reply could be noted in addition to the unclassifiable group.

DEFINITIONS USED BY JUDGE IN CATEGORIZING THE RECORDS OF WHAT THE WOMEN SAID

FEELING ABOUT MENSTRUATION

Positive Groups

Very positive — Those who said "good" or "fine" with no modifying statements.

Positive — Those who said "all right," "same as usual," "no trouble at all," "pretty good," "natural," "normal," "regular," and who mentioned no complaints.

Negative Groups

Very negative — Those who used the words "terrible" or "suffering."

Negative — Those who spoke of pain, cramps, weakness, backache, sick to stomach with no accompanying positive expression of feeling.

Mixed — Those who expressed some positive feelings plus some complaint, using phrases like "all right but . . . ," "normal but." Also those who expressed mild complaints like "sleepy" or modified their complaint by saying things like "occasionally a little," "only slightly," "used to but not recently," "never much," "sometimes."

Menstrual feelings were judged by the reply only to the first question concerning feelings during menstruation. Thus a woman would be put in the positive group if she said she felt fine although later she reported some pain or discomfort when asked about these specifically.

Mixed   Those who had mixed feelings, saying rooming-in
                         was "all right but," or saying they did not want
                         the babies so soon after birth.

Wish to be a Man

Positive or Accepting   Those who said they did not wish to be a man.
Negative or Rejecting
  Negative   Those who said they had wished they were a
                         man.
  Mixed   Those who showed mixed feelings saying that
                         they sometimes wished they were a man or had
                         wished so during childbirth, or when they were
                         younger.

Satisfaction in Leading Woman's Life

Positive or Satisfied   Those who said that women had a better or more
                         satisfying time in life.
                         Those who said that satisfaction in life depends
                         on circumstances other than sex or that men and
                         women have about the same amount of satisfac-
                         tion.
Negative or Unsatisfied Those who said that men have a more satisfying
                         or better time in life or that woman's role is
                         worse, giving general or no reasons for their
                         opinion.
                         Those who said men have a more satisfying time
                         in life because they do not have babies.

Personal responses using "I" and "my husband" were treated in the same
way as if the more general terms had been adhered to. When two categories
of responses were given, the classification of the most extreme group was
given.

Enjoyment of Sexual Intercourse

Enjoyed   When woman stated sexual intercourse was enjoy-
                         able, all right, etc., at least at certain times and
                         under certain circumstances.
Not Enjoyed   When woman spoke of dislike or acquiescence for
                         husband's sake or avoided saying intercourse was
                         enjoyable at least under certain circumstances
                         or at certain times.

Desired Frequency of Sexual Intercourse

Frequent	Married women who said they liked to have intercourse twice a week or more provided the statement was unmodified by negative remarks.
Infrequent	Married women who said they liked to have intercourse less than twice a week or those who hesitated about twice a week with remarks like "twice a week is plenty" or "twice a week because of my husband."

Eliminating Clues that Might Introduce Bias

The record of every interview was cut into nine pieces with the case number written on the back of each piece. Each piece contained the mimeographed questions about one area of feeling and the original verbatim notes of the mother's replies to this one area of feeling. The feeling areas being measured were separated* from one another and could not influence judgments directly or indirectly. Thus the slip of paper which contained the material about breast feeding gave no indication of how the mother had felt about birth. Nor was there any way of telling whether the woman who said she felt men had a more satisfying time in life also said she wished to be a man.

Judging the Words of the Mothers

The words of the mothers were sorted into categories by a judge who did not know the mothers, and who was not trained to speculate about psychological innuendoes. He was presented with definitions of the categories pertinent to one area of feeling and with the pieces of the interview records which dealt with that area of feeling. He referred to the definitions constantly, but their spirit rather than their exact verbiage was used to determine the placement of feelings that bordered on the edge of the two categories. He was instructed not to look at the case numbers on the back of the pieces. His judgments were accepted as final and were the only ones used in this research. The judge not only classified the material into evaluative groups but also decided which replies were so vague or lacking in essential information that they were unclassifiable.

Reliability of the Judgments

The objectivity of the final definitions and the reliability of the categorization is suggested by the fact that 90 per cent agreement was procured between the judge and the investigator. The check was conducted in the

* Due to the exploratory nature of the interviews on intercourse, the two expressions of feeling about intercourse were not separated from one another.

following manner: The investigator chose ten slips at random from each of the groups of feelings that were expressed in the interview. She sorted these slips into positive, negative and unclassifiable categories, making 110 judgments in all. After they were classified, she looked at the record of how the judge had classified them. In some of the feeling categories they agreed 100 per cent of the time and their rate of agreement never fell below 80 per cent for any of the feeling areas categorized. The reason for such a high rate of agreement may have been that the definitions tended to be couched in concrete objective language rather than vague abstract terms.

THE MEANING AND ACCURACY OF THE POSITIVE AND NEGATIVE GROUPS

Although the women's feelings about their biological role were put into positive and negative categories, it should not be assumed that these feelings were actually purely negative or positive. Obviously most human beings have mixed feelings about most experiences. Even the most negative mother would probably have had something positive to say about birth if she had been induced to talk about the subject at great length, and the most positive mother would probably have brought forth some negative statements.

However, there is good evidence to believe *that as a group* the negative groups represented more negative feeling than the positive groups, and vice versa. Evidence for this can be found not only in the later behavior of the mothers, but also the fact that some findings are corroborated by another person.

Seventy per cent of the "positive feelings toward breast feeding" group were feeding their babies completely by breast at six weeks. Only 32 per cent of the "negative feelings toward breast feeding" group were totally breast feeding at six weeks. Considering that the latter group includes those mothers who said they desired to breast feed for a month or two, this difference in percentage shows a substantial correspondence between measured feelings and later performance of the mother.

Agreement was also found between reports of menstrual pain recorded in the prenatal clinic and feelings toward menstruation expressed in the interview. Eighty-five per cent of the women reporting no menstrual pain were later judged to have positive feelings toward menstruation. Sixty per cent of those women reporting menstrual pain were later judged to have negative feelings toward menstruation. Considering that the data were assessed by entirely different people, under different circumstances, and after time and the experience of childbirth had intervened, this is a high rate of agreement, especially since somewhat different aspects of menstrual feelings were being judged.

An almost identical question to the one used in this study was used by the *Fortune* Survey in 1946. The *Fortune* Survey asked: "If you could be born over again would you rather be a man or a woman?" Twenty-five per cent of all the women responded that they wished they were a man. In this research the wished-to-be-men group comprised 28 per cent of those whose opinions were available. Thus there is excellent agreement between this study and another one conducted under entirely different circumstances and on a national scale.

REFERENCES

1. BORING, E. G. *et al.* *Introduction to Psychology.* New York, Wiley, 1939.
2. CAMERON, N. *The Psychology of Behavior Disorders; A Biosocial Interpretation.* Boston, Houghton, 1947.
3. MUNN, N. L. *Psychology: The Fundamentals of Human Adjustment.* Boston, Houghton, 1946.

APPENDIX C

THE STATISTICAL METHODS

MEASURE OF RELATIONSHIP

Phi correlation coefficients were used to give a measure of the degree of relationship between each two items studied. The magnitude of the phi correlation coefficient ranges from 1.00 through zero to -1.00. A phi coefficient of .00 means that there is no relationship. It means that how mothers measured on one item had nothing to do with how mothers measured on the other item. Plus one would mean a perfect positive relationship with all positive mothers remaining positive on the second item and all the negative mothers remaining negative on the second item. Minus one would mean a perfect negative relationship with all the positive mothers becoming negative on the second item and all the negative mothers becoming positive on the second item.

The phi correlation coefficient is a product moment correlation coefficient. Phi coefficients were calculated by the following formula:

$$\phi = \frac{ad - bc}{\sqrt{(a+b)(c+d)(a+c)(b+d)}}$$

Where $a, b, c,$ and d represent the following cells in a Two-by-Two Table.

	Positive Group	Negative Group
Positive Group	a	b
Negative Group	c	d

MEASURE OF PROBABILITY

Most people would be willing to bet some money on a race if they knew they had four out of five chances of winning ($p=0.20$) or nine out of ten chances of winning ($p=0.10$). They would bet more if they had nineteen out of twenty chances of winning ($p=0.05$) and still more if their chances of winning were ninety-eight or ninety-nine in a hundred ($p=0.02$ or $p=0.01$).

For this reason five different levels of significance were calculated ($p<0.20$, 0.10, 0.05, 0.02, and 0.01). These represented the different levels of confidence that could be placed on the results.

Level of significance was calculated by obtaining the Chi-square from the following formula:

$$X^2 = N\phi^2$$

ϕ was carried to three decimals to eliminate rounding errors. In cases where the predicted frequency in any one cell was less than five, Yates' correction for continuity was applied and the Chi-square recalculated. When this yielded a probability level lower than the original Chi-square, probability was calculated by the direct method to determine the exact probability level of the phi correlation coefficient.

APPENDIX D

STATISTICAL DETAILS OF THE FINDINGS
OF THIS RESEARCH

DETAILED STATISTICS ABOUT FEELINGS TOWARD MENSTRUATION

When compared with women who expressed positive feelings toward menstruation *women who expressed negative feelings toward menstruation showed some tendency to*
—wish for boy babies (N=89; $\phi=-.24$; $p<.05$)
—wish to be men (N=110; $\phi=.13$; $p<.20$)
—dislike looking after their babies in the hospital (N=121; $\phi=.20$; $p<.05$)
—say that more children in the family are "ideal" (N=101; $\phi=-.29$; $p<.01$)
—have fewer children (N=119; $\phi=.27$; $p<.01$)
—be younger (N=121; $\phi=.30$; $p<.01$)
—report much more pain during menstruation (N=108; $\phi=.45$; $p<.01$)
—report that their menstrual periods lasted longer (N=113; $\phi=-.17$; $p<.10$)
—report fewer nervous symptoms six weeks postpartum (N=37; $\phi=-.39$; $p<.05$)
—have more miscarriages (N=87; $\phi=.18$; $p<.10$)
—have more abnormal births (N=120; $\phi=.22$; $p<.02$)
—have anesthesia and/or analgesia at birth (N=120; $\phi=.13$; $p<.20$)

DETAILED STATISTICS ABOUT FEELINGS TOWARD PREGNANCY

When compared with women who expressed positive feelings toward pregnancy *women who expressed negative feelings toward pregnancy showed some tendency to*
—wish to be men (N=108; $\phi=.23$; $p<.02$
—dislike looking after their babies in the hospital (N=119; $\phi=.16$; $p<.10$)
—be completely unreconciled to sex of baby (N=87; $\phi=.23$; $p<.20$)
—be older women (N=119; $\phi=-.22$; $p<.02$)

125

—say that fewer children in the family are "ideal" (N=100; ϕ=.13; p<.20)
—have more normal births (N=118; ϕ=−.19; p<.05)
—have no anesthesia and/or analgesia at birth (N=118; ϕ=−.15; p<.20)
—have babies who gained weight rapidly (N=105; ϕ=−.17; p<.10)
—be of lower income-occupation groups (N=104; p<.10)

DETAILED STATISTICS ABOUT FEELINGS TOWARD CHILDBIRTH

When compared with women who had positive feelings about childbirth, *women who expressed negative feelings toward birth showed some tendency to*
—prefer artificial to breast feeding (N=108; ϕ=.28; p<.01)
—dislike looking after their babies (N=112; ϕ=.25; p<.01)
—have fewer children (N=111; ϕ=.19; p<.05)
—have more abnormal births (N=111; ϕ=.16; p<.10)
—be of lower or higher income-occupation groups rather than semiskilled groups (N=100; p<.10)
—have anesthesia or analgesia at birth (N=111; ϕ=.17; p<.10)

DETAILED STATISTICS ABOUT FEELINGS TOWARD BREAST FEEDING

When compared with women who expressed positive feelings toward breast feeding, *women who expressed negative feelings toward breast feeding showed some tendency to*
—think childbirth was hard (N=108; ϕ=.28; p<.01)
—feel men have a more satisfying time in life (N=89; ϕ=.21; p<.05)
—complain about having to care for the baby (N=119; ϕ=.16; p<.10)
—be less successful breast feeding in the hospital (N=93; ϕ=.16; p<.20)
—use artificial methods of feeding six weeks after birth (N=42; ϕ=.38; p<.02)
—have longer labors with their first babies (N=24; ϕ=.52; p<.05)
—want girl babies, instead of boy babies (N=87; ϕ=.20; p<.10)
—be of higher or lower occupational groups rather than the semiskilled group (N=104; p<.10)

DETAILED STATISTICS ABOUT FEELINGS TOWARD CARE OF BABY

When compared with women who expressed positive feelings about the care of their babies, *women who expressed negative feelings about the care of their babies showed some tendency to*
—express negative feelings about menstruation (N=121; ϕ=.20; p<.05)
—express negative feelings about pregnancy (N=119; ϕ=.16; p<.10)
—express negative feelings about birth (N=112; ϕ=.25; p<.01)
—express negative feelings about breast feeding (N=119; ϕ=.16; p<.10)
—marry at a later age (N=87; ϕ=.14; p<.20)
—wish to be men (N=112; ϕ=.14; p<.20)
—report less copious menstrual flow (N=113; ϕ=.31; p<.01)

—have more previous miscarriages (N=89; ϕ=.18; p<.10)
—have fewer children (N=121; ϕ=.27; p<.01)
—have anesthesia and/or analgesia at birth (N=122; ϕ=.12; p<.20)

DETAILED STATISTICS ABOUT WOMEN'S WISH TO BE A MAN

When compared with women who did not express the desire to be a man, *women who said they wished to be men showed some tendency to*
—feel men had a more satisfying time in life (N=83; ϕ=.19; p<.10)
—desire boy babies (N=80; ϕ=−.15; p<.20)
—complain about pregnancy (N=108; ϕ=.23; p<.02)
—complain about menstruation (N=110; ϕ=.13; p<.20)
—complain about the care of the baby (N=112; ϕ=.14; p<.20)
—be married and living with husband (less illegitimate children)
     (N=109; ϕ=−.21; p<.05)
—have more children (N=110; ϕ=−.13; p<.20)
—breast feed successfully in the hospital (N=87; ϕ=−.20; p<.20)
—continue to breast feed at six weeks (N=37; ϕ=−.35; p<.10)
—have less copious menstrual flow (N=102; ϕ=.14; p<.20)
—work after marriage (N=43; ϕ=.30; p<.05)
—be older (N=112; ϕ−.24; p<.01)
—be Catholic rather than Protestant (N=86; ϕ=−.19; p<.10)
—belong to skilled or semiskilled occupation groups (N=97; p<.20)

DETAILED STATISTICS ABOUT WOMEN'S FEELINGS THAT MEN HAVE A MORE SATISFYING TIME IN LIFE

When compared with women who did not feel men had a more satisfying time in life, *women who said they felt men had a more satisfying time in life showed some tendency to*
—wish to be men (N=83; ϕ=.19; p<.10)
—want boy babies (N=67; ϕ=.19; p<.20)
—prefer artificial feeding (N=89; ϕ=.21; p<.05)
—have anesthesia and/or analgesia at birth (N=90; ϕ=.16; p<.20)
—have more children (N=86; ϕ=−.17; p<.20)
—report less pain during menstruation (N=83; ϕ=−.23; p<.05)
—report more copious menstrual flow (N=83; ϕ=−.29; p<.01)
—be older (N=91; ϕ=−.14; p<.20)

DETAILED STATISTICS OF THE EXPLORATORY STUDY ON
FEELING TOWARD INTERCOURSE

	Phi coefficients[a] showing the relationship of *enjoyment of sexual intercourse* to other aspects of women's feelings	Phi coefficients[a] showing the relationship of desired *frequency of sexual intercourse* to other aspects of women's feelings
Feelings about menstruation	.02 (23)	.34 (18)
Feelings about pregnancy	.23 (23)	.38 (17)
Feelings about childbirth	−.03 (22)	.01 (18)
Feelings about breast feeding	−.28 (23)	−.40 (17)
Feelings about care of baby	.00 (24)	−.12 (18)
Acceptance of womanhood	.04 (20)	.27 (16)
Satisfaction in leading woman's life	−.02 (21)	−.58[b] (15)

[a] The numbers of women involved are in parentheses.
[b] The probability of this relationship occurring by chance is .10-.05.

DETAILED STATISTICS OF THE EXPLORATORY STUDY SHOWING
RELATION OF BIOLOGICAL AND CULTURAL FEMININITY

	Number of women for whom usable data were available on both variables	*Phi-coefficient showing relationship of cultural femininity[a] to women's feelings about their biologically determined role*	
Feelings about menstruation	26	.08	
Feelings about pregnancy	26	−.32	($p<0.30$)
Feelings about childbirth	25	−.14	
Feelings about breast feeding	25	.13	
Feelings about care of baby	26	.00	
Acceptance of womanhood	24	−.51	($p<0.04$)[b]
Satisfaction in leading woman's life	20	.35	($p<0.23$)[b]
Enjoyment of sexual intercourse	16	−.07	
Desired frequency of sexual intercourse	15	−.21	

[a] Cultural femininity was measured by scores on the Terman M-F test.
[b] This probability was calculated by the direct method in order to get a more accurate assessment of probability level.

INDEX

Abortions and miscarriages
cultural attitudes toward, 69
and feelings about menstruation, 19
influence of hypnosis on, 17
and motherly feelings, 63
ABRAMSON, M., 34
Adjustment, emotional
and breast feeding, 50
maternal care, 67
menstrual pain, 17
see also Nervous symptoms *and* Neurotic personality
Age differences
and feelings toward menstruation, 19
toward pregnancy, 27
importance of, 9
marriage, variations with feelings toward baby care, 62
and satisfaction in women's life, 76
and wish to be man, 76
AMATRUDA, C. S., 65
Amenorrhea, *see* Menstrual flow *and* Menstrual cycle
American Board of Obstetrics and Gynecology, 19
American Institute of Family Relations, 91
Analgesia, *see* Anesthesia
Anesthesia and analgesia during labor
cause of asphyxia in baby, 37
cooperative childbirth, amount given in, 33, 40
time of giving, 32
effect on normality of labor, 37
previous childbirth experiences influencing, desire for, 34

Anesthesia and analgesia—*Continued*
Swedish attitude toward, 38
use of, as related to
feeling toward birth, 36, 37
toward menstruation, 19, 37
toward pregnancy, 27, 38
mother love, 37, 63
see also Cooperative childbirth
Anthropologist, 2, 3
Anxiety
during breast feeding, 49
and menstrual flow, 18
menstrual pain, 16
in pregnancy, 26
ARISTOTLE, 5, 6
Atlantic, 39, 40
Attitudes, *see* Feelings

Baby, *see* Child *and* Feelings about sex of baby
BAGG, H. J., 51
BAKWIN, H., 63, 65
Baltimore, 64
Bataan, 15
BEARD, M. R., 95-96
Bell Adjustment Inventory, 16-17
Bellevue Hospital, 64
BENEDEK, T., 15
BEVAN-BROWN, M., 65
BILLINGS, E. G., 15
Biological femininity, *see* Femininity
Biological functions, *see* Reproductive functions
Birth
harmful effects, 30, 36
memory of experience during, 34
mind-body relationship in, 30-36, 39-40, 105

129

Birth—*Continued*
normality of, and
anesthesia and analgesia used, 37
cooperative childbirth, 33, 37
feelings about menstruation, 19
about pregnancy, 27
orgasm, similarity to, 87
quotations of mothers about, 35
social attitudes toward, 1, 3, 31, 34, 38-40, 68, 85, 89, 92
tears and cuts due to psychological causes, 39
see also Anesthesia, Cooperative childbirth, Feelings toward birth, *and* Labor
Birthrate
reflection of parental love, 82
and women's work, 97
BLACKSTONE, 96
Bleeding, *see* Menstrual flow
BOWLBY, J., 67
Breast feeding
of adopted babies, 44, 60
as antithesis to sexual intercourse, 90
and baby's "security," 49
cause of confused thinking about, 48
encouragement of, 54
and heterosexual feelings, 51, 89
influence on mother-child relationship, 49-51
mind-body relationships, 43-48, 49-51
and motherly feelings, 46
as part of obstetrics, 39
physical influence on baby, 52-54
on mother, 50-52
psychologically caused disorders
early weaning, 55
milk expulsion failure, 45, 55
nipple pain, 45
secretion failure, 44, 55
social attitudes towards, 1, 3, 39, 49, 53-55, 68, 82, 83, 90, 92
successful, nature of, 49
and wish to be man, 76
see also Feelings toward breast feeding *and* Milk production
Britain, 53
British Medical Journal, 11

CAHEN, A., 91
CAMERON, N., 113
Canada, 82
CANNON, 31
Care of baby, *see* Maternal care

Catholic faith, variation with wish to be man, 76
CHAPIN, H. D., 64
Child
breast feeding of adopted, 44
development and intelligence
breast vs. bottle fed, 52
when lacking motherly care, 65
emotional adustment
breast vs. bottle fed, 49
when lacking motherly care, 66
health
breast vs. bottle fed, 52, 54
when lacking motherly care, 63-65
psychosomatic relation to mother, 92
rejection, of bottle by, 44
of breast by, 44
weight gain
variation with mother's feelings about pregnancy, 27
when lacking motherly care, 63, 66
see also Number of children
Childbearing, *see* Reproductive functions
CHILDERS, A. T., 50
Class differences, *see* Socioeconomic differences
CLEOPATRA, 96
Coitus, *see* Sexual intercourse
Conclusions, *see* Summary
Contraceptive measures
breast feeding as, 52
husband's vs. wife's right to decide when used, 78
relation to sexual adjustment, 91
voluntary infertility after birth trauma, 30
Cooperative childbirth
compared with hypnosis, 34
definition of, 31-32
difficulties that prevent popularity, 38, 68
international movement, 4
at Jefferson Hospital, 8
physicians' attitudes toward, 38, 68, 108, 115
physiological similarity to sexual intercourse, 87-89
statistical evaluations of, 32-34
in Sweden, 38
techniques of, 32, 39
theories behind, 31
women's attitudes toward, 4, 38, 83

Cooperative childbirth—*Continued*
see also Anesthesia, Birth, Feelings
toward birth, *and* Labor
Corregidor, 15
Counseling, *see* Psychotherapy
Cultural attitudes
in modern America toward
baby care, 1, 3, 67
birth, 1, 3, 31, 34, 39, 40, 68, 85,
89, 92
body secretions, 45
breast feeding, 1, 3, 39, 49, 54, 55,
68, 82, 83, 85, 90, 92
menstruation, 1, 3, 21, 82, 85, 92
motherhood, 1, 68-69, 82
pregnancy, 1, 3, 31, 82, 85, 92
women, 73-75, 77-80, 96, 98
in other cultures toward
baby care, 60
birth, 3, 38-40, 89
breast feeding, 3, 39, 49, 53, 55
menstruation, 3
pregnancy, 3
women's role, 95, 96-98
Cultural femininity, *see* Femininity
CUNNINGHAM, R. L., 16

DeLEE, S. T., 25
Depression
caused by lack of motherly care, 63
during menstrual cycle, 14
variation with menstrual flow, 15
DERSHIMER, F. W., 31
DEUTSCH, H., 3
Diet
in breast feeding, 55, 56
influence on motherly behavior, 60
in pregnancy, 31, 60
Doctor, *see* Physician
DUNBAR, H. F., 17
Dysmenorrhea, *see* Menstrual pain

Education
for doctors, 19, 38, 69, 115
for fathers, 33, 61
increase in, influence on mother's
work, 97
for mothers, 9, 31, 34, 39, 54, 61, 68
Egypt, 52
Elation
after childbirth, 37, 40, 88
during menstrual cycle, 14
after sexual intercourse, 88
variation with menstrual flow, 15

ELY, F., 46
Emotions, *see* Feelings
England, 4, 47
Envy of men, 73-84
ambivalence of women who show,
76, 81
dangers of, 81
hopeful trends in, 82
importance of, 77, 81, 102
methods of meeting problem, 82
possible causes of
attitude of employers, 79
dependence, 80
family life, 77
men's dislike of successful women,
98
sexual differences, 3, 80
socioeconomic factors, 80
unequal pay, 79
ways of viewing problem, 81
see also Satisfaction in leading woman's life *and* Wish to be man
Episiotomies, psychological causes of,
39

Family
finances, as related to envy of men,
73, 74, 77, 78, 80
government allowances for, 82
life
as cause of envy of men, 77
psychosomatic aspects of, 92
women's changing role in, 96
support of, influence on job equality,
82
tax concessions for, 82
see also Marriage *and* Number of
children
FARNHAM, M. F., 96
Fathers
children, growing interest in, 83
classes for, 33
feelings toward children, variations
with
hormonal influence, 50
intelligence, 61
marriage happiness, 61
social class, 61
psychosomatic relation with family,
92
sexual desires after parenthood, 91
see also Family *and* Marriage
Feelings; *see entries below, and* Cultural attitudes, Envy of men,

Feelings—*Continued*
Heterosexual feelings, Interview, Measurement of feelings, Motherly feelings, *and* Rapport
Feelings toward baby care
definitions, 62, 118
and feelings toward men, 62
toward reproductive role, 62
as index of motherly feelings, 62
and menstrual flow, 63
and obstetrical problems, 63
positive and negative groups compared, 62, 126
see also Motherly feelings
Feelings toward birth
and anesthesia, 36, 37
comparison of positive and negative groups, 35, 126
definition, 35, 117
fear of, relation to sex adjustment, 89
importance of, 30, 36, 102
joy·at birth, 3, 37, 40, 88
and physical affection for baby, 35
and physical and social factors, 35
range of, 35
see also Birth, Cooperative Childbirth, *and* Labor
Feelings toward breast feeding
ambivalence in women who wish to be men, 76, 81
and amount of milk given baby, 44, 45, 48
and baby's behavior at feeding times, 44
comparison of positive and negative groups, 47, 126
definitions, 47, 118
and duration of labor, 48
and feelings toward reproductive role, 48
and heterosexual feelings, 90
importance of, 54, 102
and incidence of nipple damage, 44
and need for supplemental feeding, 43, 46, 48
and reproductive efficiency, 48
restriction of enjoyment, 90
and socioeconomic factors, 48
strong negative feelings, 47, 54
positive feelings, 56
and use of nipple shield, 44
see also Breast feeding

Feelings toward menstruation
definitions, 18, 116
and feelings toward men, 18
importance of, 21, 102
and heterosexual feelings, 86
key to understanding personality, 21
and motherly feelings, 18
and obstetrical problems, 19
and physical course of menstruation, 19
positive and negative groups compared, 18, 125
psychotherapy for, 20
see also Menstrual pain
Feelings toward pregnancy
and attitudes toward men, 27
and baby's weight gain, 27
comparison of positive and negative groups, 27, 125
cultural attitudes, influence on, 31
definitions, 26, 117
and economic factors, 26, 27
and femininity test score, 99
and heterosexual feelings, 87
importance of, 27, 102
inadequacy of knowledge about, 27
and motherly feelings, 27
and physical course of childbirth, 27
see also Pregnancy
Feelings about sex of baby
dislike of sex of baby, variation with feelings toward pregnancy, 27
wish for boy baby, variations with feelings toward breast feeding, 48
toward menstruation, 18
satisfaction in woman's life, 75
wish to be man, 75
see also Motherly feelings
Female role, *see* Femininity *and* Women
Femininity, 95-101
biological
definition of, 99
historical trends favoring, 95
sources of, 98
cultural
definition of, 98, 99
historical trends favoring, 96
sources of, 98
and feelings toward pregnancy, 99
and menstrual pain, 16
Newton's theory
expounded, 96-99
tested, 99

Femininity—*Continued*
  psychoanalytic theories, 2, 3
  and satisfaction in woman's role, 99
  and wish to be man, 99
  see also Envy of men *and* Women
Feminism
  fallacy of, 82
  source of misleading theories, 96
Fertility
  and divorce, 91, 97
    marriage happiness, 91
    numbers of marriages, 91
    sexual adjustment, 91
    woman's other work responsibilities, 97
Findings, *see* Results of this study, Review of literature, *and* Summary and conclusions
FITZGERALD, J. E., 24
Fortune Survey
  finding of, 73-75, 77-80, 82, 98, 121-122
  as research tool, 74
FREED, S. C., 17
FREEMAN, M., 46, 47
FREUD, S., 3
FRIES, M., 105-106
Frigidity, *see* Heterosexual feelings

GALEN, 5, 6
GESELL, A., 65
  development schedule, 66
GOLDFARB, W., 66
Greeks, 19
Gynecology
  advantage of, in obtaining expression of personal feelings, 21, 106
  psychological techniques useful in, 28, 105, 106, 107, 109
  training in, 19, 115

HALL, D. E., 26
HAMAN, J. O., 17
HAMIL, B. M., 50
HARDY, M. C., 50
HARNIK, M., 16, 18
Harvard, 80
HARVEY, 6
Hate, *see* Feelings
Health, 2
  influence, of bottle and breast feeding, 51-54
    of maternal care on, 63, 65
  of mother, 60

Health—*Continued*
  physician's care in good, 69
  in pregnancy, 31
  in women with menstrual pain, 16
Heterosexual feelings, 85-92
  and act of breast feeding, 51-89
  definitions used in this research, 119, 120
  and envy of men, 76, 81
  and fear of childbirth, 89
  and fear of having children, 91
  and feelings during childbirth, 88
    toward breast feeding, 48, 90
    toward menstruation, 86
    toward pregnancy, 87
  and menstrual cycle, 14, 86
    pain, 16, 86
  and month of pregnancy, 86
  and motherly feelings, 92
  and nausea of pregnancy, 25, 86
  need for more research, 92
  and nipple stimulation, 90
  and number of children, 91
  and ovulation, 86
  results of this study, 86, 87, 89, 90, 92, 128
  review of literature, 85-91
  and sterility, 91
  see also Sexual intercourse
HEYER, G. R., 17
Hippocratic Oath, 11
HIRST, J. C., 26
HOEFER, C., 50
HOLWAY, A. R., 50
Hormones and female behavior, 60
  and estrogen, 15
    oxytocin, 45, 46, 48, 50, 89
    progesterone, 15
    prolactin, 46, 50
HORNEY, K., 3
Hospitalism, 63-65
HUNTER, W. E., 18
Husband
  classes for, 33
  with mother during labor, 32
  see also Marriage
Hyperemesis gravidarum, *see* Nausea
Hypnosis
  effect on menstruation, 17
  method of shortening labor, 34
  in treating vomiting of pregnancy, 25

IBM, 10

Immaturity
  emotional
    in children deprived of maternal
      care, 65
    in mothers, 69
    in vomiting of pregnancy, 25
  physical, in dysmenorrhea, 16
Indian, American, 25
Interview
  environmental setting of
    general considerations, 107
    in this research, 108
  mode of questioning in
    general considerations, 109
    how developed in this research,
      109
    standardized questions used, 110-
      112
  technique, 8, 105-112
  time of
    general considerations, 105
    in this research, 106
  type of data obtained by, 9
  see also Rapport

JEFFCOATE, T. N. A., 30, 36
Jefferson Hospital, 8, 11, 67
Job, see Work
JOHNSON, G. B., 15

KINSEY, A. C., 9, 85, 88, 90
KNOX, 64-65
KROGER, W. S., 17, 25

Labor
  attitude toward, in Indian women, 26
  duration of
    effect of hypnosis on, 34
    influence of obstetrician on, 33, 39
    related to desire to breast feed, 48
  environment during, 32, 34, 39
  inertia in
    cause of psychological trauma, 30
    caused by anesthesia and analgesia,
      37
  management of second stage of, 39,
    40
  pain in
    causes of, 31, 36
    in cooperative childbirth, 33, 38,
      40
    degree of, 35, 36
    methods of relief, 36-38
    pharmacological, 36, 37

Labor—Continued
  pain in—Continued
    psychological, 31, 34, 36, 38
    psychological effect of, 30, 36
    position in, 32, 39
    see also Anesthesia, Birth, and Co-
      operative childbirth
Lactation, see Breast feeding and Milk
  production
LANDIS, J. T., 86, 89, 91
Let-down reflex, 45, 50, 55, 89
LEVY, D. M., 46, 59, 60
LOESER, A. A., 16
LORAND, A., 34
Love, see Feelings
LUFF, 14, 15, 85-86
LUNDBERG, F., 96

McBRYDE, A., 61
McCANCE, R. A., 14, 15, 85-86
Marriage
  counseling, 70, 104, 115
  dislike of successful women in, 98
  division of responsibility and rights
    in, 77, 80
  equality in history, 95
  happiness, related to
    envy of men, 81
    love of children, 61
    number of children, 91
  see also Women
Masculinity-Femininity test, see TER-
  MAN, L. M.
MASLOW, A. H., 50
Masochism, 3
  see also Breast feeding, Femininity,
    Labor, and Menstrual pain
Maternal care
  healing influence on sick baby, 64, 66
  in hospitals, 61, 67, 68
  importance of, 63
  as index of motherly feelings, 62
  influence on health of child, 63-65
    on psychology of child, 65-67
  social attitudes toward, 1, 3, 68, 69,
    82
  see also Feelings toward baby care
MEAD, M., 3, 60
Measurement of feelings, 9, 10, 113-122
  bias in
    methods of avoiding, 115
    research on, 113
    types of, 114

Measurement of feelings—*Continued*
  methods used in this research
    briefly described, 9, 10
    definitions used by judge, 116-120
    eliminating clues, 120
    finding pattern of reply, 116
    Masculinity-Femininity test, 10,
      112
    method of judgment, 120
  reliability and validity
    cooperation of mothers
      objective measure, 109
      subjective measure, 108
    findings, compared to *Fortune* Sur-
      vey, 121
    compared with medical records,
      121
    of judgments, 120
Men
  envy of women in, 80
  importance of women's feelings to,
    81, 104
  see also Envy of men, Father, *and*
    Wish to be man
MENNINGER, K. A., 16
Menorrhagia, *see* Menstrual flow
Menstrual cycle
  alterations of
    by emotional trauma, 16
    by hypnosis, 17
  effect on
    activity, 15
    behavior, 14
    emotions, 14
    heterosexual feelings, 14, 86
    intellectual processes, 15
    work, 15
  psychotherapy for disorders of, 17,
    20
  see also Menstrual flow *and* Men-
    struation
Menstrual flow
  effect of
    emotions on, 15
    hypnosis on, 17
  and feelings toward baby care, 63
    toward menstruation, 19
  and motherly feelings, 59
  psychotherapy for disorders of, 17, 20
  and satisfaction in woman's life, 76
  and wish to be man, 76
  see also Menstrual cycle *and* Men-
    struation

Menstrual pain
  effect of hypnosis on, 17
  emotional adjustment of women with,
    17
  and feelings toward menstruation,
    19
  and heterosexual responsiveness, 16,
    86
  immaturity in women with, 16
  occurrence in neurotic personalities,
    16
  psychotherapy for, 17, 20
  and satisfaction in women's life, 76
  resentment of femininity in women
    with, 16
  see also Feelings toward menstrua-
    tion
Menstruation
  menarche, 2, 3, 20
  menopause, 3
  menstrual history, psychological im-
    portance of, 20-21
  mind-body relationships in, 14-19
  social attitudes towards, 1, 3, 21, 82,
    85, 92
  see also Feelings toward menstrua-
    tion, Menstrual cycle, Menstrual
    flow, *and* Menstrual pain
MEYERS, C. S., 15
Middle Ages, 95
Midwives, 69
Milk production
  as affected by
    excitement, 44, 55
    hospital practices, 55
    milk expulsion reflex, 45
    nipple care, 45
    sucking stimulation, 44, 55
  and cultural attitudes toward breast
    feeding, 45, 49, 54, 68
  and desire to breast feed, 43, 48
  see also Breast feeding
MILLER, H. L., 33, 34, 39
Miscarriages, *see* Abortions
MOHR, G. J., 26
Morning sickness, *see* Nausea
Mother
  counseling for, 69
  education of, 9, 31, 34, 39, 54, 61,
    68
  heterosexual feelings in, 91
  "home" for, 68, 70
  influence on daughter's pregnancy, 25
  need for more income for, 82

Mother—*Continued*
  psychosomatic importance of, 92
  social attitude's "devaluation" toward,
      3, 60, 69, 82, 96
  sudden loss of, 66
  unmarried
    nausea in pregnancy of, 24
    acceptance of unborn baby, 26
  see also Child, Motherly feelings,
      Number of children, *and* Women
Motherly feelings
  in animals, 46, 50, 60, 99
  attitudes toward, modern American,
      69
  importance of, 63, 68, 102
  methods of improving, 68-70
  and psychological factors
    early home life of mother, 61
    marriage happiness, 61
    mother's, age at marriage, 62
      envy of men, 62
      feelings toward birth, 35, 62
      feelings toward breast feeding,
          48, 56, 62
      feelings toward menstruation,
          18, 62
      feelings toward pregnancy, 24,
          27, 62
      number of children in family,
          27, 61, 63
  and social factors
    education of mother, 61
    socioeconomic factors, 61
  special love of son, 81
  variations with physical aspects of
      mother
    body build, 60
    breast feeding, 46, 50
    childbirth trauma, 30, 35, 37, 40,
        68
    diet, 60
    hormonal changes, 60
    menstrual flow, 59, 63
    month of pregnancy, 26
  see also Feelings about sex of baby,
      Feelings toward baby care,
      and Maternal Care
Multiparas
  cultural difference in incidence of
      tears and cuts of perineum, 39
  greater need for gas, 34
  need for anesthesia in cooperative
      childbirth, 33
  see also Number of children

Narcissism, 3
  see also Femininity
National Research Council, 56, 60
Natural childbirth, *see* Cooperative
    childbirth
Nausea and vomiting, in pregnancy
  in American Indian women, 25
  cured by hypnosis, 25
  and emotional dependence, 26
  and number of children previously
      produced, 24
  psychotherapy for, 28
  and rejection of child, 24
  and socioeconomic factors, 24
  and unwanted intercourse, 25, 87
  variability in successive pregnancies,
      25
Negative feelings (emotions, attitudes),
    see Feelings
Negro, *see* Race differences
Nervous symptoms
  and feelings toward menstruation, 19
    lack of maternal care, 66
    menstrual cycle, 14
    menstrual pain, 16
  see also Adjustment *and* Neurotic
      personality
Neurotic personality
  and menstrual pain, 16
  and penis envy, 3
  symptoms of, in cultural femininity,
      98
  see also Adjustment *and* Nervous
      symptoms
New York State, 64
NEWTON, M., 43, 44, 45, 46, 48, 89
NEWTON, N., 43, 44, 45, 46, 47, 48, 49,
    50, 89
NOVAK, J., 16, 18
Number of children
  and breast feeding, duration of, 47
  considered "ideal," variations with
    feelings toward menstruation, 19
    feelings toward pregnancy, 27
  and feeling of satisfaction in life, 76
  and marital happiness, 91
  and mother's feelings, toward baby
      care, 61, 63
    toward childbirth, 35
    toward menstruation, 19
    toward pregnancy, 27
  and traumatic labors, 30
  and wish to be man, 76
  see also Family

Obstetrics
  breast feeding as part of, 39
  techniques useful in, 28, 31, 39, 54-
    56, 68, 105, 106, 107, 109
  training in, 19, 38, 69, 115
Occupation, *see* Socioeconomic differ-
    ences *and* Work
Orgasm, *see* Heterosexual feelings *and*
    Sexual intercourse
Overprotection, *see* Feelings toward
    baby care *and* Motherly feelings

Passivity, 3
  in animal mothers, 99
  in women, 3, 98
  see also Femininity
PAYNE, S. M., 2
Pediatrics
  techniques useful in, 54-56, 68-70,
    105, 106, 107, 109
  training, 69, 115
Penis envy, 3, 80, 107
  see also Envy of men
PETERSON, W. E., 44, 45, 46
PETERSON, C. H., 50
Phi correlation coefficients, *see* Statistics
Philadelphia, 8
Philippines, 15
Physicians
  attitude toward
    breast feeding, 54-56
    childbirth, 36, 38, 69, 108
    faith in large numbers, 11
    importance of women's feelings to,
      104
    role in care of healthy women, 69
  see also Gynecology, Obstetrics,
    Pediatrics, *and* Psychiatry
POPENOE, P. 91
Positive feelings (emotions, attitudes)
  see Feelings
Practical applications of study
  all-over findings, 102
  biological vs. cultural femininity, 100
  birth emotions, 36-40
  breast feeding emotions, 48-56
  envy of men, 77-83
  menstrual emotions, 19-21
  motherly emotions, 63-70
  pregnancy emotions, 27
  research needed, 6, 27, 50, 61, 68,
    81, 92, 100, 102, 105
  sexual emotions, 92

Pregnancy
  anxiety during, 26
  dislike of, 26
  effect of fear of, 16
  fear of, caused by childbirth trauma,
    30
  importance of, to women, 2, 3, 27
  mind-body relationships, 24-27
  psychotherapy during normal, 28
  social attitudes toward, 1, 3, 31, 82,
    85
  variation with sexual desire, 86
  see also Abortions, Feelings toward
    pregnancy, *and* Nausea
Primiparas
  anesthesia, need of in cooperative
    childbirth, 33
  cultural differences in incidence of
    tears and cuts of perineum, 39
  length of labor as related to breast
    feeding attitudes, 48
  see also Number of children
Protestant faith, as related to wish to
    be man, 76
Psychiatry, need for
  in maternal problems, 70
  in menstrual problems, 20
  see also Psychotherapy
Psychoanalysis, 2, 7, 15
Psychologist, 6, 21, 104
Psychology, *see* Psychotherapy
Psychoses
  influence on menstrual flow, 15
  precipitated by childbirth, 30
  by separation from mother, 66
Psychosomatic relationships, 5, 7, 102
  see also Results of this study *and*
    Review of literature
Psychotherapy
  for breast feeding, 54-56
  during normal labor, 31, 39
  education in treating
    menstrual disorder, 17, 20
    vomiting of pregnancy, 25, 28
  for motherhood, 68-70
  for normal pregnant women, 28, 32
  vs. drug therapy during labor, 36-38
  see also Hypnosis

Race differences
  absence of in this research, 8
  in Kinsey research, 9
  in nausea of pregnancy, 24
  and choice of rooming-in at Yale. 61

Race differences—*Continued*
and pay for work, 79
as factor in rapport, 107
Rapport
factors influencing, 105-107
importance of, to physicians, 21, 28
problems of establishing, 107
in this research, 9, 108, 121
READ, G. D., 3, 31, 33, 37, 39, 40,
88-89
REED, R., 26
Rejection, *see* Feelings about sex of
baby, Feelings toward baby care,
and Motherly feelings
Reliability, *see* Measurement of feelings
Reproductive functions
cultural attitudes toward, 1, 3
importance of, 2
interrelation of feelings towards, 1,
21, 37, 48, 62, 68, 82
see also Birth, Breast feeding, Menstruation, Pregnancy, Maternal
care, *and* Sexual intercourse
Research methods, 5-13, 105-124
brief summary of, 7-13
case for controlled statistical, 5
experiment in maternal love, 62
exploratory study, 10, 112
general principles, 5-7, 105-109, 113-
116, 124
limits imposed by, 11, 60, 102
psychosomatic approach, 7
review of literature as part of, 12
see also Definition of terms, interview, Measurement of feelings,
Rapport, Sampling, *and* Statistics
Results of this study
biological vs. cultural femininity, 99,
128
envy of men, 75, 127
feelings toward breast feeding, 47,
126
toward childbirth, 34, 126
toward menstruation, 18, 125
toward pregnancy, 26, 125
heterosexual emotions, 86, 87, 89,
90, 92, 128
limits of, 11, 102
motherly emotions, 62, 126
statistical details, 125-128
verbally expressed, 18, 26, 34, 47,
62, 75, 86, 87, 89, 90, 92, 99
see also Review of literature

Review of literature
changes in women's status, 95-98
envy of men, 73-75, 77-80
psychosomatic aspects of
breast feeding, 43-47, 49-51
childbirth, 30-34, 36, 37, 39
menstruation, 14-18
motherliness, 59-61, 63-68
pregnancy, 24-26
sexual intercourse, relation to
women's reproductive role, 85-92
women's sexuality, theories about,
2-4
RHEINGOLD, H. L., 66
RHINE, 7
ROBERTSON, G. G., 24, 25, 86-87
ROLF, B. B., 18
Rooming-in, 8, 61, 67
see also Feelings toward baby care
and Maternal care
ROSE, A. A., 16
RUBENSTEIN, B. B., 15

Sampling
bias in, 6, 33
limitations of, 11, 102
women studied, 8, 9
San Francisco Charities Clinic, 65
Santo Tomas Internment Camp, 15
Satisfaction in leading woman's life
definition used
in *Fortune* Survey, 74
in this research, 75, 119
and efficiency in reproduction, 76
and feelings toward men, 74, 75
toward reproductive role, 76
and femininity test score, 99
and heterosexual feelings, 76
money management, 74
positive and negative groups compared
Fortune Survey group, 74
this research, 75, 127
social factors, 76
see also Envy of men, *and* Femininity
Sex, *see* Feelings about sex of baby *and*
Sexual intercourse
Sexual Behavior of the Human Female,
85
Sexual intercourse, 85-92
antithesis to breast feeding, 90
attitudes of modern American culture
toward, 85

Sexual intercourse—*Continued*
extramarital intercourse, attitude of
society toward, 78
frequency of
cause of pregnancy nausea, 25
varying during menstrual cycle, 15,
85
similarity with
physiology of breast feeding, 89
of childbirth, 87
see also Heterosexual feelings
SMITH, A. J., 15
Social workers, 104
Society, attitudes of, *see* Cultural attitudes
Socioeconomic differences, as related to
feelings about birth, 36
about breast feeding, 48
about ease of woman's life, 74
about pregnancy, 27
about rooming-in, 61
health of bottle babies, 53
rejection of child, 61
satisfaction in women's life, 76
wish to be man, 76, 81
South Africa, 4
SOWTON, S. C. M., 15
SPANO, F. L., 50
SPENCE, J. C., 51
SPITZ, R. A., 64, 65, 66
Statistics
Chi square
formula for, 124
use of, 10, 124
limits of applicability, 11, 102
methods used, 10, 123
number of women used, 8, 11
Phi correlation coefficient
formula for, 123
meaning of, 123
use of, 10
results, 125-128
significance, levels of
rationale behind choice, 10, 124
use of, 11
STROUSSE, F., 26
Summary and conclusions
envy of men, 83
feelings toward birth, 40
feelings toward breast feeding, 56
feelings toward menstruation, 21
feelings toward pregnancy, 29
femininity, types of, 100
general, 102

Summary and conclusions—*Continued*
motherly emotions, 70
research methods, 12
sexual emotions, 92
theories about maternal emotions, 4
women's status in history, 100
SUTTIE, I. D., 65
Sweden, 4, 38
SYMONDS, P. M., 61
Szilagyi-Kessler, I., 50

TERMAN, L. M.
Masculinity-Femininity test, 10
administration, 109, 112
results, 99, 128
study, 91
THOMPSON, L. J., 26
THOMS, H., 37
TOMPKINS, W. T., 60

United States, 4, 11, 19, 52, 55, 61, 65
Census, 1, 91, 96, 97
Unmarried mothers, *see* Women

Validity, *see* Measurement of feelings
Vomiting, *see* Nausea

Waller, H. K., 45
WARDEN, C. J., 99
Weaning
age, measure of motherliness, 47
early, 49, 55
gastrointestinal disturbance at, 53
late, 56
sudden, 50, 81
WEBSTER, A., 24
WHITE, C., 11
WIDDOWSON, 14, 15, 85-86
WILSON, A. T. M., 16, 91
Wish to be man
definition used
in *Fortune* Survey, 74
in this research, 75, 119
and efficiency in reproductive role, 76
extent of, 77
and feelings toward reproductive
role, 76
and femininity test score, 99
and money management, 73
and other feelings toward men, 73,
75
positive and negative groups compared, 73, 75, 127
and social factors, 76

Wish to be man—*Continued*
  and unmarried motherhood, 76
  and work, 73, 76
  see also Envy of men
WITTKOWER, E., 16, 91
Women
  abilities
    as influenced by menstruation, 15
    social attitudes towards, 73, 74, 79,
      96, 98
  attitudes toward cooperative child-
    birth, 38
  dependence of
    before industrial revolution, 95, 96
    in modern America, 80, 96
  differences between married and un-
    married
    in acceptance of pregnancy, 26
    in envy of men, 76
    in heterosexual feelings, 15, 86
    in pregnancy vomiting, 24
  different ways of viewing, 82, 96, 99
  discrimination against, 1, 3, 77-80,
    82, 96, 98
  ease of life, as related to social class,
    74
  inferiority feelings in, 3, 78, 82, 98

Women—*Continued*
  losses in recent years, 96
  psychoanalysts, 2
  role in history, 95
  as source of sexual theories, 2, 92
  see also Envy of men, Femininity,
    and Mother
Work
  after marriage, variations with wish
    to be man, 76
  conflict with maternal care, 70
  distrust of women for job of responsi-
    bility, 79, 80
  home, for mothers, 82
  and menstrual cycle, 15
  opportunity, theory of equality of,
    73, 82
  pay difference for men and women
    with same educations, 79
    with same type of job, 79
  psychological effect of, 96
  rights of medieval guild women, 95
World Health Organization, 67
World War II, 15
WYATT, R. H., 37

Yale, 33, 34, 39, 61, 80
YATES, 124